toward more effective science instruction in secondary education

Hans O. Andersen

ASSOCIATE PROFESSOR OF SCIENCE EDUCATION
INDIANA UNIVERSITY

Paul G. Koutnik

PROGRAM COORDINATOR, DEVELOPMENT OF INQUIRY SKILLS
MID-CONTINENT REGIONAL EDUCATIONAL LABORATORY
KANSAS CITY, MISSOURI

toward more effective
science instruction
in secondary education

The Macmillan Company NEW YORK
Collier-Macmillan Limited LONDON

preface

An examination of the vast quantities of materials used by secondary science education instructors forces one to conclude that it is impossible to include all of the pertinent material in a single volume. In fact, it may not even be desirable to attempt it. This volume was designed to contain an introduction to many of the ideas that science teachers need to plan effective science instruction. It should be a useful source of information to both preservice and in-service science teachers.

The first three chapters explore a definition of science relevant to science teachers, a definition of teaching relevant to science, and objectives for science teaching. Chapters 4 through 8 deal with planning, implementing, and evaluating science instruction. The remaining chapters treat issues that secondary school science teachers face or will face sometime during their careers.

Admittedly, this is not a complete treatment of all the topics a secondary school science teacher should study. It is, in fact, but one of five books published by The Macmillan Company which deal specifically with secondary school science instruction. The readers of this volume are encouraged to examine *Readings in Science Education for the Secondary School* and three companion sourcebooks—*Sourcebook for Chemistry and Physics*, *Sourcebook for Earth Sciences and Astronomy*, and *Sourcebook for Biological Sciences*—that have been prepared to supplement this one containing methods.

v

Space limitations prevent our acknowledging everyone who assisted us. However, we are particularly indebted to the undergraduate students who read and criticized drafts of the chapters, especially those who suffered through first drafts of the chapters. Additional credit is given to our graduate students, who helped us by providing alternate points of view and experimental background materials, and to the region laboratory program development staff members, especially Richard M. Bingman. Mr. Lloyd Chilton, our editor, and Ronald C. Harris, our production editor, similarly must be cited for their encouragement, criticisms, and the skills they employed turning our manuscript into a book.

For reading the galley and page proofs, we are indebted to Sandra Andersen. For assistance in every dimension, we shall forever be indebted to Sandra Andersen and Carol Koutnik.

H. O. A.
P. G. K.

contents

vii

**toward more effective
science instruction
in secondary education**

a definition of science relevant to science teaching

It has been the authors' experience that many high school students and lay adults view science as an enterprise which advances our living standard through the mechanism of breakthroughs. Advanced science students frequently react to this perception of science by separating engineering, or applied science (which may be immediately responsible for helping us live well), from "real," or basic, science (which may reveal consistencies in the way nature operates so that others may engineer practical applications).

We will not be concerned here with erecting artificial barriers between science and engineering. Few who call themselves scientists pursue their work without considerable knowledge of engineering, and many engineers regularly deal with basic problems. Both types, more importantly, operate within fields which advance by breakthroughs, the nature of which depends not on additional observations or evidence, but on reorientations in the minds of the men credited with the breakthroughs.

Breakthroughs as New Perspectives

H. Butterfield, the Cambridge historian, makes much of this reorientational sort of breakthrough.[1] He ascribes to it the major change in scientific thought constituted by the primitive theory of impetus, which developed in

[1] H. Butterfield, *The Origins of Modern Science* (New York: Macmillan, 1956), pp. 1–12.

the face of sixteenth- and seventeenth-century Aristotelian explanations of motion.

The Aristotelian doctrine of inertia held that a body would stay in motion *only so long as a mover was in actual contact and imparting motion to it.* So set was this doctrine that marvelously contrived explanations were offered for nearly all of what seemed to be exceptions. The continued motion of projectiles, such as flying arrows after leaving the bow or cannon shot after leaving the barrel, was accounted for by the rush of air from the apex of the projectile (where it was being compressed) to the rear, where a *vacuum must not be allowed!* The rush itself was the force in constant contact with the moved object and was believed to produce the acceleration which resulted after the arrow, for instance, had left the bowstring.

Such a combination of faulty premises (mover must always contact the moving, making it always a "moved" object when not at rest) and a sort of teleological anthropomorphism (vacuum must not be allowed) was common in this system of explanation. How could one consider freely moving bodies in a resistanceless vacuum (a necessary antecedent to formulating even primitive hypotheses of modern mechanics) if some fluid had to be there to supply a motive "rush"?[2] Indeed, vacuums not only did not occur in daily experience, they could not exist!

It is tempting for us to say, "Had the Aristotelians observed more rigorously, they would have seen the errors in their notions." We might also argue that pre-Victorian observers must certainly have come up with evolutionary hypotheses upon repeatedly encountering what *we* know to be fossil remains of ancient life. But the sixteenth-century Aristotelian *einstellung* was the way of the day. Generations had matured within a system of explanation and rationalization which held very little difference between assumptions and conclusions. Nature was not at fault, nor was observation. No more data was required. What was required was a mind which could take other than a popular position and view the same phenomena from a different position.

Many would agree that substitution of a theory of impetus (only initial contact needed to set bodies in motion) for the doctrine of Aristotle and perception of fossils as fossils (not as tricks of a supreme intelligence) were breakthroughs in their times from which whole new systems of thought evolved. Eventually a Newton would bring mechanics to flower with the application of mathematics. Then an Einstein would look at many of the *same* kinds of data, but from an entirely new perspective of relativistic mechanics. Note that

---

[2] See ibid., Chapter 1, for a thorough treatment of the development of an anti-Aristotelian theory of impetus.

it was not the discovery of startlingly new phenomena which changed our observations of nature in the case of these significant scientific breakthroughs. Mind changed.

Science and Inquiry

A. D. Ritchie, in his description of scientific method, has attempted to define science in a fashion which conveys the process rather than a product orientation.[3] In so doing, he represents it as the process of exploring the external world. And this is not a random exploration. It depends on what Ritchie refers to as *active observation.* There is a specific interest which limits (that is, *controls*) the scope and focus of the observation. Thus active observation is experimentation. An active observation may approach ideal limits (that is, perfect controls) of scope and focus.[4] To this extent it is an experiment. But note the purposive attempt to limit the observation. The observer simply wants to observe something specific.

The Biological Sciences Curriculum Study, in addition to other recently developed science curricula, has emphasized inquiry as a learning objective for science instruction. BSCS texts and supplementary materials in use in thousands of schools have been designed to support, among other concepts, "Science as Inquiry and Investigation."[5] This concept is important to the BSCS and is one of ten major themes intended to pervade the entire curriculum. This and other attempts to present science and inquiry as synonyms may help us to get closer to a definition of science by suggesting that we consider inquiry. Mid-continent Regional Educational Laboratory and the BSCS developed a definition and elaboration of inquiry which McREL published as its initial position paper. The "Rationale" from this document, *Inquiry Objectives in the Teaching of Biology,* appears below.[6]

---

[3] A. D. Ritchie, *Scientific Method, An Inquiry into the Character and Validity of Natural Laws* (Patterson, N.J.: Littlefield, Adams, 1960), p. 14.

[4] Ibid., pp. 21–22.

[5] John A. Moore et al., *Biological Science: An Inquiry Into Life* (New York: Harcourt, Brace, 1963), p. 9.

[6] *Inquiry Objectives in the Teaching of Biology*, Richard M. Bingman, ed., McREL Position Paper, Vol. 1, No. 1 (September, 1969), p. 1. Mid-continent Regional Educational Laboratory; 104 East Independence Avenue; Kansas City, Missouri 64106.

Inquiry theory and behaviorally stated objectives for inquiry learning have been elaborately stated in various BSCS-related publications, including *Inquiry Objectives in the Teaching of Biology*. The equivalent of *IOTB* does not seem to exist for others of the traditionally separated high school sciences. Hence, reference is made primarily to biology in the area of inquiry definition and objectives. The authors, however, hold that this discussion should be as effective with substitution of the name of any high school science, including, simply, "science." We urge the reader to use the "science" substitution regardless of his

RATIONALE

The Substantive Knowledge of Biological Science

The current substantive body of biological knowledge includes the knowledge of inquiry processes and the findings of these inquiries. While it is true that they are inseparable and probably are equally important, for many years in educational practice the findings of inquiry (content) have been heavily emphasized to the exclusion of inquiry processes. Recently emphasis has been placed on the inquiry processes; however, many biology teachers are not familiar with them. For these reasons, it is appropriate that inquiry processes now should be given a great deal of attention. This attention should not exclude or foreshadow the importance of teaching the findings of scientific inquiries. As a matter of fact, teaching inquiry processes demands the teaching of content inseparable from process.

The Nature of Inquiry and Its Relation to the Organization and Use of This Document

Inquiry, as defined in this document, is a set of activities directed towards solving an open number of related problems in which the student has as his principal focus a productive enterprise leading to increased understanding and application.

Success in any particular inquiry involves some, but probably not all, possible inquiry behaviors and skills. There is no attempt in this report to prescribe a definite order of inquiry skills and behaviors for any inquiry activity or for any time during a biology course. The biologist in conducting biological research, or the student in carrying out inquiry processes in the classroom, may not exhibit behaviors in the order listed. It is also understood that at the beginning of a course the student will possess certain information, cognitive skills, and attitudes that are necessary in inquiry activities. These will be applied and built upon throughout the inquiry activities.

The nature of inquiry is complex; inquiry engages the skills, interests, and attitudes of the person in an interaction with the substantive and cognitive demands of a problem as he makes efforts to cope rationally with it. Inquiry activities may vary in form and sequence from one problem to another and from one person to another person. Successful inquiry need not necessarily be terminated with the attainment of a solution to a problem, nor is the solution necessarily essential for inquiry to be deemed successful.

In the second paragraph of the preceding quote comes one of those gems of definition that says a universe in a sentence. Note first that inquiry is defined as a set of activities. Further on, any casual attempt to interpret this as *the* set or *the* order is foiled. In addition, the set is *directed* and has a productive enterprise as its focus (recall the purposive limitation of Ritchie's active observation). The inquirer is in the business of trying to increase his *understanding* and his *application* of that understanding. McREL-BSCS inquiry has

---

personal disciplinary bias or the authors' choice of examples. To cover inquiry philosophy on an "equal-time" basis in each of the disciplines would likely be intolerably redundant to the reader.

a direction and focus. Furthermore, a blow may be dealt to the "pure"-science-vs.-engineering separatists when we see inquiry as directed toward increased understanding *and* application. Hence a somewhat more specific definition of science than Ritchie's but still quite encompassing would be, "Science is inquiry."

If the synonym holds, then the immediate objectives of science would be the solution of a specific number of problems in an effort to increase understanding and application. The open number of problems is a must for the inquirer-scientist who may not anticipate accurately the number and nature of all problems he will encounter. But what of the *set of activities* and the disclaimer of a specific order?

Follow the Steps?

Only a few years ago nearly all science texts contained in their prefaces or first chapters a set of ordered steps known as the scientific method. Perhaps the reader has been exposed to such linear methods through secondary or college science texts. Occasionally, course lecturers have advocated "the method" in their orientation lectures. The authors' experience is that such advocacy is a reliable prediction that the course which follows will not contain science as we have been attempting to define it, let alone any following of "the method." The scientific method usually started with a problem, went from there to hypotheses, to deductive or implicative reasoning, to designing and executing a system of data collection (often an experiment), to interpreting data, and finally to conclusions. Some variations appeared on this theme, but the prescribed linear path from problem to conclusion was nearly always there.

Because the conclusions of science are arranged in an orderly way in the literature as taxonomies and theoretical structures of the various disciplines, it stood to reason that the process which originally exposed the knowledge was also orderly. Furthermore, it was proposed, if we wished to produce more scientists or have learners do things in scientific ways, we ought to teach an ordered process for getting a job done.

Granted, the layman is less likely to run astray from an intended outcome if he operates within a linear series of steps than if he behaves randomly. The occasional cook is also better off to read the cake-mix instructions than to charge about with pots, mix, fire, and water. The error would be, of course, in calling these people scientist-inquirers and chefs.

Rather than being good at "the order," scientists and creative chefs are more likely to be *really good* at certain basic processes of inquiry applied in their respective areas. Not only are they likely to be skilled at process application, but they are likely to understand the significance of a given process in terms of producing results and in terms of its relationship to other processes. Moreover, they have come to value skilled process application not only for its results but in the way a professional values a skill itself and seeks to build proficiency in its use. The fundamental error in "classical" advocacy of the scientific method was not so much in the particular "steps" constituting basic processes or necessary behaviors of scientists as it was in the way they were presented as steps.[7] The work of Butts and others has not revealed patterned (that is, stepwise) thought to exist to any reliable degree in problem-solving behavior.

If we move from a search for a magic method or generalizable pattern and still wish to find out what makes good scientists and inquirers, we are left with the skills, understandings, and attitudes that they bring to bear on a problem. Although more complex than orders of steps, the skills, understandings, and attitudes of scientists and inquirers are still within reach of the student and can be targets of good teaching.

Scientific Objectives for Learners

We have given attention to the "different way of looking" at common things that has probably accounted for some of the most significant breakthroughs in science. Then we considered and rejected patterned scientific method, which left applying, understanding, and valuing (attitude) the "basic skills" of scientists and inquirers. (Recall that the "basic skills" we refer to include such operations as interpreting, observing, hypothesizing, designing and executing investigations, and defining problems, though not necessarily in a reliable order of occurrence.) What we have is a combination of creative and critical thinking (that is, the divergent view and inquiry skills).

It should follow that if science instruction is to provide learners with a realistic view of science, it should provide opportunities and active support for comprehension and application of basic skills to the acquisition of increased understanding. Furthermore, it must encourage divergence and the

[7] David Butts, "The Relationship of Problem Solving Ability and Science Knowledge," *Science Education*, Vol. 49 (March, 1965), pp. 138–46. Of the various studies which have attempted to shed light on the steps–no-steps question, none would be more relevant for the reader at this time than that of Butts. Butts was able to conclude from findings in his study that there is no relationship between a person's knowledge of facts and principles of science and his problem-solving behavior when that behavior is evaluated according to the degree to which it displays specific patterns.

development of predispositions to view issues from various perspectives, including those of other individuals or groups. In such instruction the learner's primary objective is increased understanding. (As such, no stigma need be attached to being "wrong" or accepting someone's opinion other than one's own if increased understanding results.)

We hypothesize that the success and reward experiences associated with application of basic skills and divergent observation in an environment relatively free of threats to the self are likely to aid learners to be sensitive to and objective about information, ideas, ideologies, and institutions in society. But we observe that "science" class, or any other activity in the school day, is but a small amount of the total influence in the life of the learner. How many schools are organized as centers of inquiry? How many homes offer internships for budding inquirers? Before closing these covers in acceptance of an insurmountable obstacle, consider the following propositions for science and its instruction as a potentially revolutionary force in the lives of children and schools.

Self-actualization

People who have little respect for their own potential lead miserable lives. Nothing is more tragic than a student who has no confidence in his own ability to perform and feels that others value him similarly. Not only do all students develop differently with respect to ability to apply basic skills of observation, inference, and interpretation, but the mere acceptance of their differences by teacher and class smooths the way for us to allow them to exhibit any divergence in their use of these skills. As we have advocated, divergence in expression is something to be encouraged, and the mere fact that much of a student's divergence could be accounted for in terms of level of sophistication, "intelligence," and so on, should not overly concern us. What we do not want is for any student to keep silent for fear he is "not with it" (that is, not sophisticated, not smart, and so on). The "not-with-itness" may be a major component of science. Support and encouragement of creativity and critical thinking can have terrific impact on children who, perhaps for the first time, start to value themselves as individuals capable of understanding and demonstrating that understanding to others in a way they see as important to others.

Science Can Be Many Things in School

Science, defined as a combination of applied inquiry skills and a predisposition to view available things from unusual perspectives, is more of a generalizable collection of behaviors, understandings, and attitudes than a group of academic disciplines with "scientific" names ending in -*ology* or -*ics*. As such we offer the proposition that any subject matter area in which inquiry and divergent observation have operated together to have produced the generally recognized major increments in development of the area may be a scientific one. Without too much trouble one could, accepting this, produce an argument for nearly the whole curriculum of the school being science and inquiry oriented, where the same student skills are objectives of the many disciplines and the total program of a school is coordinated to develop creative and critical thinkers.

Your initial teaching assignment may not be in such a center of inquiry, but this need not release you from the obligation to represent your area of science in a way consistent with science itself. Other parts of this book will deal with theories and technologies of science instruction. It is enough here to advocate learning objectives in the creative and critical thinking domains of science as we have attempted to define it.

Discussion Questions

1. Describe a "divergent" observation or breakthrough that you have experienced in your attempts to gain understanding or application of science.
2. State what you would consider to be the most important goal of secondary school education (or education of youth in general). Then defend teaching of either (a) a sequence of traditionally separated secondary school sciences (biology, chemistry, physics, and so on) or (b) an integrated interdisciplinary curriculum, such as science 1, science 2, science 3, and so on.
3. Must some exposure to secondary school science be required of every student? Why, or why not?
4. Prepare a defense paper entitled "Why Science in Our Curriculum?" for presentation to a hypothetical PTA group. If you changed the word *science* to some other discipline, say, social studies, how would your paper need to be changed? Considering the statement called for in the first sentence of question 2, are your changes, if any, consistent with education's most important goal?
5. The school in which you teach has a policy which excludes academically unsuccessful students from all science courses except Daily Health. Assume and describe a basis for determining whether a student is "unsuccessful." Assume and describe a set of objectives for Daily Health students. Recall your answer to question 4. Explain why you support or reject your school's exclusion policy.
6. Write your recollection of the "scientific method" as you have heard it described in science courses or read about it in textbooks. Compare your paper with those of others in your class.
   Visit several professors engaged in research to ask if they do it in some way consistently similar or dissimilar to your recollection of the "method."

7. Have you included self-actualization in your defense paper (question 4)? If not, try to incorporate this concept. Also, include advice to parents on how to reinforce this important concept at home.
8. Does a process-vs.-content polarity exist in your class? Can each individual, including yourself, rationalize his position with respect to his own statement in question 2?

a definition of teaching relevant to science

Good teaching must be defined in terms of the degree and kind of change caused in students. That is, good teaching is not simply a mechanical operation which can be defined in terms of a teacher's looks, his speaking voice, the neatness of his room, and the fact that he never sends anyone to the principal. Although each of these characteristics may contribute to teaching success, they are not the substance of good teaching. Good teaching occurs when students learn the subject that is to be taught and desire to learn much more about the subject.

Another characteristic of good teaching is that it is something an individual does, and although any individual may be a good teacher in a given situation with a given student, he may fail miserably in another situation with the same student. Teachers, of course, have twenty-five or more students at one time, not one. To be a good teacher the individual must be able to deal effectively with most of his students. He must be able to determine when, and to whom, he is or is not communicating. He must, like a good practitioner of general medicine, identify those students with symptoms he cannot define and treat and direct them to the appropriate specialist.

Becoming a good teacher, although difficult, is not an impossible task for most college graduates who are willing to make a concerted effort toward achieving this goal. In this chapter the writers examine a gross definition of the teaching process and some means of describing what occurs while a class is in session.

Toward a Definition of Teaching

Descriptions of what good and bad teachers can do, have done, should do, or should have done could continue indefinitely. Instead of providing training on how to become a more effective teacher, these descriptions tend to promulgate the status quo. Furthermore, relying on descriptions of how others have or should have proceeded does not specifically indicate how a different individual should teach in a different situation. It is not that carefully observing others may not be helpful. Observing a skilled teacher can be useful to individuals desiring to become excellent teachers, but like any expert advice it should be a guide to, but never a substitute for, one's own thinking. Simply stated, *carbon copies are never as clear as the original.* The truly effective teacher will view each teaching situation as a new problem demanding an original and unique teaching strategy. The individual teacher must design or select each strategy he employs in his instruction, and each design or selection should be based on his interpretation of what he thinks will constitute effective instruction for his particular population. His individual interpretation should, whenever possible, be based on empirical evidence, past experience, and extensive knowledge of methods and materials.

The role of the teacher, as it is defined in the previous paragraph, revolves around the process of selecting effective instructional strategies. An instructional strategy is defined as something a teacher arranges that is designed to establish interaction between the teacher, the students, the subject matter, or any combination of these three dimensions. As a selector of instructional strategies, the effective teacher will

1. Plan to influence directly or indirectly the learning process by varying his behavior.
2. Tailor the subject matter to meet the needs and interests of each individual.
3. Arrange a variety of media, including books, lecture notes, homework, visual aids, programs, discussions, and laboratory experiences.

This model of effective teaching places the student in the center completely surrounded by multisensory media arranged by the teacher, who functions as a prescriber-organizer. The teacher, acting as a prescriber-organizer, studies each student's physical and mental characteristics as well as his previous achievement record. Then he hypothesizes and prescribes the next educational experience for the student. This is followed by another evaluation and another prescription. If the prescription is successful and the student is able to demonstrate the hypothesized terminal performance, he will be directed to a new experience in a new area. If the prescription is not successful the student will be directed to repeat it or he might be directed to a similar experience in another media.

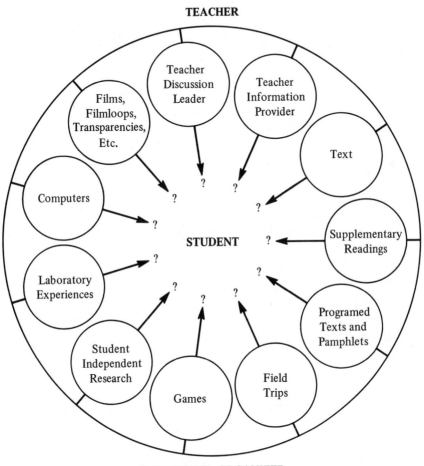

TEACHER

PRESCRIBER–ORGANIZER

Figure 2-1. The teacher as a prescriber-organizer.

Arranging conditions or selecting strategies which will produce the desired degree of interaction between student, subject matter, and teacher can also be seen as a dual function. First, the affective tone must be established; second, the subject matter and media must be arranged. This simplification permits diagraming the teaching act as a neat cyclic structure, but it

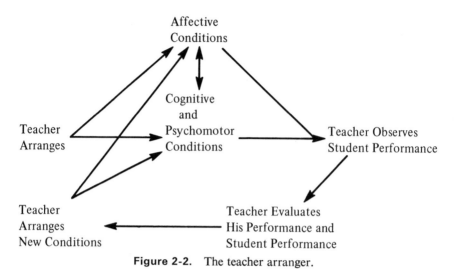

Figure 2-2.   The teacher arranger.

may neglect the potential interaction between the affective and cognitive–psychomotor conditions.

The significance of developing the optimal affective tone is derived from the role a student's attitude plays in governing the amount of energy utilized in a given activity. High-level intellectual activity does not usually

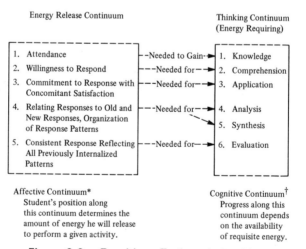

Figure 2-3.   Cognitive–affective relationships.

* David R. Krathwohl et al., *Taxonomy of Educational Objectives Handbook II: Affective Domain* (New York: David McKay, 1956).

† Benjamin Bloom et al., *Taxonomy of Educational Objectives Handbook I: Cognitive Domain* (New York: David McKay, 1956).

occur unless the student's attitude toward the pursuit induces him to release the energy needed to complete the activity. The following diagram illustrates the connection between the affective and cognitive continua and exemplifies the relationship between availability of energy and the potential extent of cognitive activity.

The teacher who wants his students to operate in the upper levels of the cognitive and affective continua must consistently emulate these levels through his own teaching acts. To do this he should

1. Be an active teacher who will exhibit a strong emotional tone. Students learn more from active than from passive teachers and from teachers with a strong emotional tone, whether this tone is positive or negative.
2. Respect students as individuals capable of intellectual activity and provide them with the opportunity to engage in such activity.
3. Plan carefully and extensively, but view each lesson as a hypothetical construct rather than as the one and only path. Effective planning uncovers many alternative paths. Effective teaching involves moving each student along a path of least resistance into positions where he may integrate and associate ideas.
4. Evaluate his teaching actions on every possible dimension.

Planning and arranging strategies, although certainly an important first step, do not constitute the completed teaching act. Furthermore, relying on written examinations as the final proof of teaching success may be similarly misleading. Evaluation should accompany each step of the teaching process.

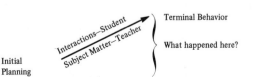

Figure 2-4. Planning, interactions, and terminal behaviors.

Simply stating that the strategies look good, or that the students were able or not able to attain a given level of mastery does not reveal the strengths and weaknesses of the interactions which occurred between initial planning and final evaluation.

The interactions between student, subject matter, and teacher are many and varied. Quantitatively describing the nature of these interactions permits the teacher to analyze his actions and the actions of students. A teacher so equipped may then choose to modify his influence and quantitatively describe how the change influenced student behavior.

What Happens in the Classroom?

Three different interaction analysis instruments will be described on the pages which follow. Two of the instruments are designed for classroom situations involving considerable amounts of teacher talk. The third instrument is designed for use in a laboratory setting where teacher talk is minimal.

*Categories for Interaction Analysis**

Teacher Talk	*Indirect Influence*	1. *Accepts feeling:* Accepts and clarifies the feeling tone of the students in a nonthreatening manner. Feelings may be positive or negative. Predicting or recalling feelings are included. 2. *Praises or encourages:* Praises or encourages student action or behavior. Jokes that release tension, not at the expense of another individual, nodding head or saying, "Um hm?" or "go on" are included. 3. *Accepts or uses ideas of student:* Clarifying, building or developing ideas suggested by a student. As teacher brings more of his own ideas into play, shift to category five. 4. *Asks questions:* Asking a question about content or procedure with the intent that a student answer.
	Direct Influence	5. *Lecturing:* Giving facts or opinions about content or procedure; expressing his own ideas, asking rhetorical questions. 6. *Giving directions:* Directions, commands, or orders to which a student is expected to comply. 7. *Criticizing or justifying authority:* Statements intended to change student behavior from nonacceptable to acceptable pattern; bawling someone out; stating why the teacher is doing what he is doing; extreme self-reference.
Student Talk		8. *Student talk—response:* Talk by students in response to teacher. Teacher initiates the contact or solicits student statement. 9. *Student talk—initiation:* Talk by students which they initiate. If "calling on" student is only to indicate who may talk next, observer must decide whether student wanted to talk. If he did, use this category. 10. *Silence or confusion:* Pauses, short periods of silence, and periods of confusion in which communication cannot be understood by the observer.

Source: Ned A. Flanders, *Teacher Influence, Pupil Attitudes, and Achievement* (Washington D.C.: U.S. Department of Health, Education and Welfare, 1965), Catalogue No. F.S. 225:25040.

* There is *no* scale implied by these numbers. Each number is classificatory; it designates a particular kind of communication event. To write these numbers down during observation is to enumerate, not to judge a position on a scale.

Flanders' System of Interaction Analysis[1]

Flanders' system of interaction analysis is used to quantify the qualitative aspects of verbal communication as they occur in the classroom. It was originally designed as a research tool to measure teacher influence.

Flanders' system, though perhaps not as functional as other more complicated instruments, can provide means for objectively determining the quantity and pattern of teacher influence. It is also much easier to use than many of the other instruments.

The Procedure

Flanders' system consists of ten totally inclusive categories. That is, all of the verbal interaction occurring during the recorded interval can be placed in one of the ten categories. Each of the categories is mutually exclusive; each of the verbalisms will fit in one and only one of the ten categories.

The system can be used by either an observer recording the action as it occurs or by a teacher listening to a tape recording of a previous class session. The procedure involves classifying each three-second communication or lack of communication as one of the prescribed set of numbered categories. The recorder listens carefully and each three seconds records the number for the type of communication that occurred. The recorder should continue at a rate of twenty to twenty-five entries per minute. When there is a major change in the classroom tempo, this can be recorded on the margin.

Tabulating the Data

After you have become familiar with the ten categories you may wish to practice using them. Listen carefully to a communication and classify each three-second communication interval into one of the ten categories. Tabulate the classifications into columns as illustrated. Begin and end each recording session with a 10.

10
6
10
7
5
1
4
8
4
10

[1] Ned A. Flanders, *Teacher Influence, Pupil Attitudes, and Achievement* (Washington, D.C.: U.S. Department of Health, Education and Welfare, 1965), Catalogue No. F.S. 225:25040.

The numbers so recorded may then be entered on a 10 × 10 matrix. The numbers are tallied on the matrix one pair at a time.

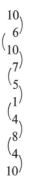

The first pair, 10–6, should be tallied in row 10, column 6 cell. The second pair, 6–10, should be tallied in row 6, column 10. The third pair, 10–7, should be tallied in row 10, column 7. The fourth pair, 7–5, should be tallied in row 7, column 5, and so on.

	1	2	3	4	5	6	7	8	9	10	Total
1				1							
2											
3											
4							1		1		
5	1										
6									1		
7					1						
8				1							
9											
10						1	1				
Total											

Figure 2-5.   Entering interaction analysis data on a matrix.

The basic totals which give a general indication of the interaction for the period of observation are

I—Sum of columns 1–4. Indirect teacher influence.
D—Sum of columns 5–6. Direct teacher influence.
S—Sum of columns 8–9. Student talk.
C—Sum of column 10. Silence or confusion.

	1	2	3	4	5	6	7	8	9	10	
1											
2											
3											
4											
5											
6											
7											
8											
9											
10											
Total											

I	D	S	C
Indirect Teacher Influence	Direct Teacher Influence	Student Talk	Confusion

Figure 2-6. Totaling matrix data.

In his study, Flanders found the following percentage figures to be typical:

Silence or confusion   0–10%
Student talk   15–40%
Teacher talk   50–80%

The information obtained from the matrix can be interpreted in several ways.

SIMPLE RATIOS (numbers refer to sums of columns)

A. The "big I/D ratio" (ratio of indirect influence to direct influence).

$$I/D = \frac{\Sigma 1 + 2 + 3 + 4}{\Sigma 5 + 6 + 7}$$

B. The "little i/d ratio" (omit sums of columns 4 and 5 in calculations).

$$i/d = \frac{\Sigma 1 + 2 + 3}{\Sigma 6 + 7}$$

(What might one I/D ratio indicate that the other omits?)

C. Student talk–teacher talk ratio.

$$\frac{\Sigma 8 + 9}{\Sigma 1 + 2 + 3 + 4 + 5 + 6 + 7}$$

Examining the Matrix

The steady-state cells are shown along the diagram from upper left to lower right. All of the pairs in the sequence which have the same number will fall along this diagonal. Such pairs occur when the speaker remains in a

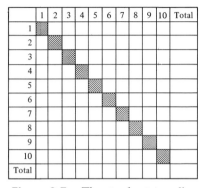

Figure 2-7.   The steady-state cells.

particular category for more than three seconds. Heavy loading in one or more of these cells may be significant. For example,

2–2 cell loading.	The teacher probably extends his praise beyond a simple "very good" to statements which include criteria for praise. A loading in this area is desirable. Longer praise statements which include the criteria for praise specifically reinforce desired behavior.
3–3 cell loading.	Often means that the teacher develops the ideas of a student with considerable care.
5–5 cell loading.	Teacher is lecturing for extended periods of time.
8–8, 9–9 cell loading.	Often indicates that the students have an opportunity to develop their own ideas.
9–9 cell loading.	Often indicates student–student communication.

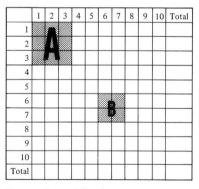

Figure 2-8.   Matrix areas A and B.

Area A is the area where the teacher's indirect influence actions would be charted. Heavy loading in this area usually indicates that the teacher is concerned with positive motivation and reward.

Heavy loading in Area B indicates that the teacher is spending a considerable amount of time dealing with student resistance. The teacher gives directions, the students resist, the teacher criticizes and then gives more directions, the students resist even more, and so on, creating a vicious circle. Heavy loading in Area B accompanied by loading in the 6–9 and 7–9 cells indicates overt resistance.

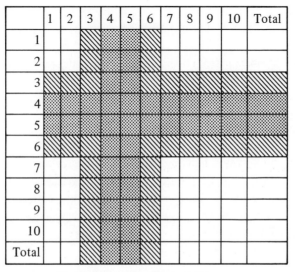

Figure 2-9. The Content Cross.

Loading in the areas shown in the Content Cross indicates an emphasis on subject matter. Asking questions and giving information may account for 70–90 per cent of what the teacher says.

The brief introduction just provided is not designed to prepare you as experts in the use of interaction analysis. It is hoped that the information provided will help you become more introspective.

A more extensive discussion of the Flanders' system of interaction analysis can be found in his monograph.

Gallagher and Aschner Model

The Gallagher and Aschner model was patterned after the structure of intellect as it was defined by Guilford. It consists of five categories which, the designers feel, enable an investigator to label teacher–pupil and pupil–pupil interaction and provides a theoretical structure that may serve as a basis for evaluating teacher behavior. Gallagher and Aschner utilized this instrument to investigate productive thought processes of gifted students as evidenced by the student's verbal interactions. Gallagher and Aschner defined productive thinking as the creative and critical-analytic actions involving convergent, divergent, and evaluative operations whereby the individual draws upon available past and present acts, ideas, associations, and observations in order to elicit new facts, ideas, and conclusions. [2,3]

The categories of this system of analysis are defined below. A more extensive discussion of the categories and additional examples of each of the question types may be found in Chapter 6.

• *Cognitive-memory* (M) operation represents the simple reproduction of facts, formulas, or other items of remembered content through the use of such processes as recognition, rote memory, and selective recall.

1. Can you give the name of a constellation, John?
2. Who discovered penicillin?
3. How did we say a hanging drop slide preparation should be made?
4. What were the main points we covered in yesterday's discussion?
5. Would you list the stages in the life cycle of a butterfly in order?
6. Is the melting of wax a chemical or physical change?
7. To which phylum does *Paramecium* belong?
8. How is Kepler's second law stated?

• *Convergent thinking* (C) represents the analysis and integration of given and remembered data. It leads to one expected end result or answer because of the tightly structured framework through which the individual must respond.

1. Would you summarize the main idea of the chapter in one sentence?
2. If you know: $F = ma$. Given that $F = 6$ newtons and $m = \frac{1}{2}$ kilogram, what is the acceleration?
3. Can you summarize the main point of the argument between the Neptunists and Plutonists?

---

[2] J. J. Gallagher and Mary J. Aschner, "A Preliminary Report: Analysis of Classroom Interaction," *Merrill-Palmer Quarterly of Behavior and Development*, Vol. 9 (July, 1963), pp. 183–94.

[3] J. P. Guilford, "The Structure of Intellect," *Psychological Bulletin*, Vol. 53 (1956), pp. 267–93.

4. This is the bacterial growth graph constructed by Laboratory Group 2. John, would you summarize your group's findings?

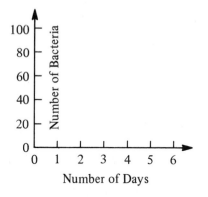

5. Can you explain what Haeckel meant when he said, "Ontogeny recapitulates phylogeny?"

• *Divergent thinking* (D) represents intellectual operations wherein the individual is free either to generate independently his own data within a data-poor situation or to take a new direction or perspective on a given topic.

1. Suppose when we woke up one morning we discovered that the CO_2 concentration in the atmosphere had tripled. What do you think the short- and long-term effects of a triple amount of CO_2 might be?
2. Suppose that a physician on board a spaceship returning from another planet states that everyone on board has disease symptoms he cannot diagnose or treat. How would you treat the spaceship and its passengers when it landed? Indicate immediate and long-term treatment.
3. You have just been hired as the scientific adviser to a community with several major pollution problems. The community has (a) a large quantity of smog, (b) reservoirs clogged with "greenish glop," and (c) water with a high bacteria count. What would you do?
4. Assume that you have extensively studied the city mentioned in situation 3. What recommendations would you make to the city planners?

• *Evaluative thinking* (E) deals with matters of judgment, value, and choice and is characterized by its judgmental quality.

1. An old man in the community says he has been watching the birds and fish and knows that there will be a very long, cold winter. Evaluate his claims using your knowledge of meteorology and biology.
2. Indicate what you think would be the best three steps that the community described with the serious air and water pollution should take to eliminate the problems.

• *Routine* (R) consists of the familiar and conventional interpersonal maneuverings of speakers in the management activities of the classroom setting.

1. Would you open the window?
2. Will you be able to complete the experiment today?
3. Did you clean up your work area?
4. Are you going to the museum this weekend?
5. Would you take this over to Bill?

To use this system the teacher classifies each question as one of the five types (evaluative, routine, and so on). A natural unit, consisting of the entire question, is used instead of a timed interval. The source of the question or statement may be indicated by attaching a t (teacher) or s (student) suffix to the code used for the communication. Because student response is usually at the same level as the teacher question (divergent questions generate divergent responses, for example), recording only the types of teacher questions will usually provide enough information for evaluation.

Some examples of the types of quantitative data which can be obtained are illustrated by the following ratios. Assume that in this case the teacher's questioning behavior is all that is being studied.

$$1. \quad \frac{\text{Questioning}}{\text{Total Teacher Verbal Performance}} = \frac{CM + C + D + E}{R + CM + C + D + E}$$

$$2. \quad \frac{\text{Productive Questioning}}{\text{Total Teacher Verbal Performance}} = \frac{C + D + E}{R + CM + C + D + E}$$

$$3. \quad \frac{\text{Productive Questions}}{\text{All Questions}} = \frac{C + D + E}{CM + C + D + E}$$

$$4. \quad \frac{\text{Cognitive-Memory Questions}}{\text{Productive Thought Questions}} = \frac{CM}{C + D + E}$$

The teacher using this system will be able to relate his subjective evaluation of a given teaching situation to the quantitative description of his questioning. Combining the subjective evaluation with the quantitative description permits the teacher to hypothesize how a modification of questioning may influence student performance.

L.I.A.I.

The Laboratory Interaction Analysis Instrument was developed by Ferrence to study interactions as they occur in the biology laboratory. The instrument was designed to be used with a three-second recording interval similar to that of Flanders. Like Flanders' system, it has a small number of categories. Teachers interested in discovering the effectiveness of their laboratory program can use this instrument to describe quantitatively the actions of students. Because this instrument was developed and validated in a rather "traditional" set of biology laboratories, it may be necessary to add categories when attempting to describe other situations. The L.I.A.I. categories and their code abbreviations include [4]

Questions: Statements eliciting answers.

Qt—*Terminology:*	Questions about the spelling or meaning of a word or group of words.
Qp—*Procedure:*	Questions indicating the student desires information and/or direction on what to do, where to find materials, or how to use materials.
Qo—*Observation:*	Questions concerning observations made or to be made.

Discussion: Examination via argument with consideration being given to the pros and cons; discoursing.

Dt—*Terminology:*	Discussion about the spelling or meaning of a word or group of words.
Dp—*Procedure:*	Discussion about the location or use of materials, operations to be performed, or actions undertaken.
Do—*Observation:*	Discussion about observations made or to be made.
R—*Reading:*	Quoting the laboratory manual or a resource text.
A—*Assignment of Tasks:*	Delegation of responsibilities to group members or activation of group.
N—*Negative Answers:*	Admission of not understanding the concept or knowing the answer.
I—*Irrelevant Discussion:*	Comments not pertinent to the laboratory investigation.

[4] Gary M. Ferrence, *The Quantification and Qualification of Verbal Communication in the High School Biology Laboratory.* Unpublished Doctoral Dissertation, Indiana University, Bloomington, Indiana, 1968, 168 pp. Copyrighted by Gary M. Ferrence. Reprinted with his permission.

T—*Teacher Talk:*   Verbalizations by the teacher.
S—*Silence:*   Periods of silence or confusion persisting for three seconds.

Arranging conditions to cause behavioral change and functioning as a prescriber of the learning experience rather than serving as an autocratic purveyor of knowledge has been defined as the teacher's major function. This definition places major emphasis on the evaluation of teaching acts and media utilized and suggests that student achievement is only one of several excellent indicators of the effectiveness of the learning situation. The effective teacher is thus defined as an individual who consistently arranges, evaluates, re-arranges, and re-evaluates, constantly working toward discovering the means to cause the maximum amount of affective, cognitive, and psychomotor development in each student.

The category systems described in this chapter are of little value if you only read about them. Even if you memorize the categories and systematically calculate the numbers of different kinds of questions you ask, or the types of interactions which occur in your laboratory, the systems may be of little value. The teacher must evaluate his influences, his questions, and all his other interactions in terms of the degree and type of behavioral change they cause. He must use the information gained to modify his influence. For example, if the discussions seem to drone on and on without arriving at the hypothesized end point, the teacher should modify his behavior. The drone may become productive conversation by the simple application of more indirect influence or the increased use of thought-provoking questions. For example, if the laboratory period consists of more irrelevant discussion than task-oriented activity, something must be changed. You might only have to reassign students to new work groups. However, you might have to revise the laboratory assignments extensively.

Using the systems to classify student and teacher behavior can give you an accurate picture of what is going on. The information and the effort used in gathering the information has little value unless you use it. Even the best teachers can improve. The use of these classification systems provides the type of reliable information a teacher needs to make decisions about modifying his teaching style or using various instructional media.

Discussion Questions

1. When is a high school teacher justified in using a lecture technique?
2. How can students shape teacher behavior?
3. Would you consider teaching some of your students how to analyze teaching and then encourage them to analyze your teaching? Why or why not?

4. If you listened to a tape recording of a lesson you taught and discovered that you were talking 70 per cent of the time and that 80 per cent of your questions were cognitive memory questions, what would you do?
5. How will you decide how much and what types of interaction are appropriate for a given lesson?
6. Write a few paragraphs and/or construct a model of the type of teacher you want to be. Then describe how you will prepare yourself for that role.

Additional References

Amidon, Edmund, and John B. Hough. *Interaction Analysis: Theory, Research, and Application.* Reading, Mass.: Addison-Wesley Publishing Co., Inc., 1967.

Anderson, R. C., G. W. Faust, M. C. Roderick, D. J. Cunningham, and T. Andre (eds.). *Current Research on Instruction.* Englewood Cliffs, N.J.: Prentice-Hall, Inc., 1969.

Brandwein, Paul F. *Building Curricular Structures for Science.* Washington, D.C.: National Science Teachers Association, 1967.

Cogan, Morris L. "Theory and Design of a Study of Teacher-Pupil Interaction," *Harvard Educational Review*, Vol. 26, 1956, pp. 315–42.

Flanders, Ned A. *Teacher Influence, Pupil Attitudes, and Achievement.* Cooperative Research Monograph, OE-25040, Washington, D.C.: U.S. Government Printing Office, 1965.

Hoover, Kenneth H. *Readings on Learning and Teaching in the Secondary School.* Boston: Allyn & Bacon, Inc., 1968.

Hough, John B., and James K. Duncan. *Teaching: Description and Analysis.* Reading, Mass.: Addison-Wesley Publishing Co., Inc., 1970.

Hyman, Ronald T. *Teaching Vantage Points for Study.* Philadelphia: J. B. Lippincott Co., 1968.

Hyman, Ronald T. *Ways of Teaching.* Philadelphia: J. B. Lippincott Co., 1970.

McLuhan, Marshal, and Quentin Fiore. *The Medium Is the Massage.* New York: Bantam Books, Inc., 1967.

Nelson, Lois N. *The Nature of Teaching: A Collection of Readings.* Waltham, Mass.: Blaisdel Publishing Co., 1969.

Raths, James, John R. Pancella, and James S. Van Ness. *Studying Teaching.* Englewood Cliffs, N.J.: Prentice-Hall, Inc., 1967.

Robinson, James T. *The Nature of Science and Science Teaching.* Belmont, Calif.: Wadsworth Publishing Co., Inc., 1968.

Romey, William D. *Inquiry Techniques for Teaching Science.* Englewood Cliffs, N.J.: Prentice-Hall, Inc., 1968.

Siegel, Laurence. *Instruction: Some Contemporary Viewpoints.* San Francisco: Chandler Publishing Co., 1967.

what should
our objectives be?

In preparing this chapter the authors were initially faced with the problem
of trying to construct a list of objectives. Each attempt resulted in the production of an endless rhetoric of elevated platitudes.

What are, or what should be, the objectives of science teaching? Of this
we are certain, objectives for science instruction, or for that matter *any* instruction, must be the individual teacher's objectives. That is, the teacher must
say, "This is what I want to accomplish. This is what I believe!" The high-
sounding rhetoric in a methods text rarely becomes more than a list of
objectives. A list of objectives that can be read passively frequently fails to
generate the emotional commitment needed to transform the list into *my* list,
my goals, *my* objectives. Hence this chapter does not contain a list of objectives. It merely contains paragraphs from a variety of sources that are intended
to arouse, but not satisfy, *your own* curiosity about *your own* objectives. Read
the paragraphs, read the original sources, think, and read some more. Then
try to answer the following questions: What *are my* objectives? How do I
want my students to visualize science?

SCIENCE AND TEACHING

An important process in the planning and development of a science curriculum is that
of identifying its purposes. These become the objectives that orient the teacher's
efforts and define the responsibilities of the learner. Objectives indicate the nature
of the educational endeavor and denote the direction it should take; they serve as a
guide for the choice of teaching procedures and provide hypotheses for making

curriculum decisions. They suggest to the teacher why his work is important, how to plan it, and how to evaluate it. Only when objectives are clearly identified and supported by a personal loyalty can the teacher maximize his efforts in the learning process.[1]

Suppose we think of our own children as planning to be nonscientists but taking some science courses as part of their general education. With what questions should we test the success of such courses? We should hardly be content to ask: How many facts have they learned? Facts are forgotten all too soon. We are more likely to ask: Can they think scientifically? Do they understand what science is about and how scientists go about their work? Have they a friendly feeling toward science and scientists? Are they likely to read scientific books in later life with enjoyment and understanding? Could they enjoy intellectual discussions with scientists? Could they work with scientific advisers in business or government?[2]

SCIENCE AN INTELLECTUAL INFLUENCE

A scientifically literate population has been cited as one of the essentials of our democratic society by educators, scientists, sociologists, anthropologists, engineers, politicians, and others.[3]

The schools and all teachers must see scientific literacy related to economic literacy, to social literacy, to humanistic literacy, to technological literacy. To educate for today only is to prepare to live for only today and is to prepare to cease to live tomorrow. To educate at the conceptual level, to help pupils see how knowledge develops, to accept the ethics of science as their own, to see science and society as interrelated, and to accept science as one of the humanities, and to see both pure and applied science as important is to prepare people to live now and in the future.[4]

An examination of the F ratios revealed that students of teachers using a larger proportion of high inquiry questions performed significantly better on both the low and high inquiry portions of the post-test examination than those students whose teachers asked a larger proportion of low inquiry questions. It was concluded that the group achievement on the post-test was significantly affected by the level of inquiry required by the teacher's questions.[5]

What is "success" in terms of developing students who are skilled in the art of investigation? The problem may be turned around so that it is operational: *What kind of school environment can we fashion that will give students the greatest oppor-*

[1] Paul DeHart Hurd, "Science Education for Changing Times," *Rethinking Science Education*, National Society for the Study of Education Yearbook, Part I (1960), p. 18.

[2] Eric M. Rogers, "The Research Scientist Looks at the Purposes of Science Teaching," *Rethinking Science Education*, National Society for the Study of Education Yearbook, Part I (1960), pp. 19–20.

[3] Milton O. Pella, G. T. O'Hearn, and C. W. Gale, "Scientific Literacy—Its Referents," *The Science Teacher* (May, 1966), p. 44.

[4] Milton O. Pella, "Scientific Literacy and the High School Curriculum," *School Science and Mathematics* (April, 1967), p. 356.

[5] George T. Ladd, *Determining the Level of Inquiry in Teachers' Questions*, unpublished dissertation, Indiana University, Bloomington, Indiana, 1969.

tunity to learn how to investigate? In the absence of tests clearly designed to select the investigator, it seems just as clear that our present road is to prepare so rich a learning environment that the student-investigator will *elect* the opportunity to investigate. *Election* of opportunity, rather than selection of students, is our bias; but not without carefully planned yet *noncoercive* identification of able students. The kind of identification we prefer occurs mainly through participation in imaginative learning, made possible by teachers who are scholars and vibrant people, as well as through formal guidance and careful testing.[6]

SCIENCE KNOWLEDGE AND KNOWING

I have had, of all people, an historian tell me that science is a collection of facts, and his voice had not even the irony of one filing cabinet reproving another![7]

Consider, first, our failure to test talents and exhibit the character of a field. Most high school and first-year collegiate courses (especially surveys and general courses) systematically convey a false impression of the fields they represent and the talents they require. They do so by almost universal use of a single device. Instead of giving experience of the kinds of problems and modes of inquiry characteristic of the field, they provide the student with the experience of assimilating, applying or otherwise using the *fruits* of inquiry in the field.[8]

Science is the attempt to make the chaotic diversity of our sense experience correspond to a logically uniform system of thought.[9]

SCIENCE AND PROCESS

The schools should help to realize the great opportunities which the development of science has made apparent in the world. They can do this by promoting understanding of the values on which science is everywhere based. Although no particular scientist may fully exemplify all these values, they characterize the enterprise of science as a whole. We believe that the following values underlie science:

1. Longing to know and to understand.
2. Questioning of all things.
3. Search for data and their meaning.
4. Demand for verification.
5. Respect for logic.
6. Consideration of premises.
7. Consideration of consequences.[10]

[6] P. F. Brandwein, J. Metzner, E. Morholt, A. Roe, and W. Rosen, *Teaching High School Biology: A Guide to Working with Potential Biologists*, American Institute of Biological Sciences (1962), p. 44.

[7] J. Bronowsky, *Science and Human Values* (New York: Harper & Row, 1959).

[8] Joseh J. Schwab, *College Curriculum and Student Protest* (Chicago: University of Chicago Press, 1969), p. 10.

[9] A. Einstein, "Considerations Concerning the Fundamentals of Theoretical Physics," *Science*, Vol. 9 (1940), p. 487.

[10] Educational Policies Commission, *Education and the Spirit of Science* (Washington, D.C.: National Education Association, 1966). Also reprinted in H. O. Andersen, *Readings in Science Education for the Secondary School* (New York: Macmillan, 1969).

What a scientist does at his desk or in his laboratory, what a literary critic does in reading a poem, are of the same order as what anybody else does when he is engaged in like activities—if he is to achieve understanding. The difference is in degree, not in kind. The schoolboy learning physics is a physicist, and it is easier for him to learn physics behaving like a physicist than doing something else. The "something else" usually involves the task of mastering what came to be called at Woods Hole a "middle language"—classroom discussions and textbooks that talk about the conclusions in a field of intellectual inquiry rather than centering upon the inquiry itself. Approached in that way, high school physics often looks very little like physics, social studies are removed from the issues of life and society as usually discussed, and school mathematics too often has lost contact with what is at the heart of the subject, the idea of order.[11]

The individual with developed rational powers can share deeply in the freedoms his society offers and can contribute most to the preservation of those freedoms. At the same time, he will have the best chance of understanding and contributing to the great events of his time. And the society which best develops the rational potentials of its people, along with their intuitive and aesthetic capabilities, will have the best chance of flourishing in the future. To help every person develop those powers is, therefore, a profoundly important objective and one which increases in importance with the passage of time. By pursuing this objective, the school can enhance spiritual and aesthetic values and the other cardinal purposes which it has traditionally served and must continue to serve.[12]

We live in a scientific civilization, whether we like it or not. Governors, lawyers, business heads, have to deal with scientists; and every educated person finds his intellectual outlook influenced by science. Yet, our science teaching of non-scientists, in school and college, has built up mistaken views, dislikes, and the common boast, "I never did understand science." Even those students who arrive at college with plans to become scientists usually bring a mistaken picture of science, something like a *stamp collection of facts or a game of getting the right answer.*[13]

SCIENCE AND SOCIETY

The philosophy of science is the same as that of humanism, except that it reverses the sequence—it begins from a sympathy with nature, and then links the human experience to that. So there is no break here between humanism and science; on the contrary, a coherent philosophy of science gives to those who grasp it a sense of man's unique place in nature that can overcome the loss of nerve or purpose which many men now feel.

The central problem in teaching today is to establish this sense of place in the

[11] Jerome S. Bruner, *The Process of Education* (Cambridge, Mass.: Harvard University Press, 1962), p. 14.

[12] Educational Policies Commission, *The Central Purposes of American Education* (Washington, D.C.: National Education Association, 1961).

[13] Eric M. Rogers, "The Research Scientist Looks at the Purposes of Science Teaching," *Rethinking Science Education*, National Society for the Study of Education Yearbook, Part I (1960), pp. 19–20.

values which science derives from its active and communal search for truth. We have to show, by example rather than precept, that the search entails of itself an ethic of human responsibility and tolerance, an aesthetic of respect and good manners, a personal dignity, which are the essence of the humanist tradition. Above all, we have to show how science has singled out from that tradition its most powerful moral: that we are judged (and indeed formed) not by the ends we proclaim, but by the means we use day by day.[14]

There have been plenty of days when I have spent the working hours with scientists and then gone off at night with some literary colleagues. I mean that literally. I have had, of course, intimate friends among both scientists and writers. It was through living among these groups and much more, I think, through moving regularly from one to another and back again that I got occupied with the problem of what, long before I put it on paper, I christened to myself as the "two cultures." For constantly I felt I was moving among two groups—comparable in intelligence, identical in race, not grossly different in social origin, earning about the same incomes, who had almost ceased to communicate at all, who in intellectual, moral and psychological climate had so little in common that instead of going from Burlington House or South Kensington to Chelsea, one might have crossed the ocean.[15]

One idea does seem quite clear: the role of science in our culture, its integration into nearly every aspect of human life and human needs, demands a revamping of science teaching to develop a coherence of science and society. The present curriculum reform has resulted in courses that are bound to scientific disciplines neglecting the social aspects of science. Glenn T. Seaborg, Gerald Holton, Frederick Sietz, Richard Meir, Eugene Rabinowitch, Bently Glass, Robert Oppenheimer, I. I. Rabi, J. Bronowsky and many other scientists have written frequently on the importance of relating the teaching of science to its larger human and cultural significance.[16]

SCIENCE AND TECHNOLOGY

Space probes, computers, automated machines, manmade satellites, tranquilizers, and plastics are technological achievements. They get considerable attention in newspapers and magazine articles; periods in civilization are named after them—space age, atomic age, age of automation, computer age—but for all of this, they represent only the "current events" of technology and indirectly, a happening in science. It is no more possible to teach science from its current events than it is to teach history from current events. The educational question involves the proper place of science and technology in high school science courses. In the curriculum reform movement the decision was to place all the emphasis upon science. None of the new science curricula lists understanding technology or its relationship to science as a goal.[17]

[14] J. Bronowsky, "Science in the New Humanism," *The Science Teacher*, Vol. 35, No. 5 (May, 1968), pp. 13–16, 72–73.
[15] C. P. Snow, *The Two Cultures and a Second Look* (New York: New American Library, 1964), p. 10. Copyright by Cambridge University Press, 1959–63.
[16] Paul DeHart Hurd, *New Directions in Teaching Secondary School Science* (Chicago: Rand McNally, 1969), p. 108.
[17] Ibid., pp. 21–22.

Moreover, the realization grew among us and among industrial and political leaders that the time fuse between discovery and application had become short and was growing shorter. The gulf between basic and applied science had narrowed, and in some instances had become imperceptible.[18]

Discussion Questions

1. What objective(s) can be inferred from the writings of each author?
2. Which objectives (two or three) do you think are the most important?
3. How would you arrange these objectives from most important to least important?
4. What additional objectives would you add to the list?
5. Would you eliminate any of the inferred objectives? Why?

Two lists of references are included with this chapter. The first is a list of magazine articles. Many of these articles are reprinted in Hans O. Andersen, *Readings in Science Education for the Secondary School* (New York: Macmillan, 1969). The second is a list of books that you will probably be able to locate in your school library.

Additional References (Articles)

Andersen, Hans O. "A Philosophy of Education for the Slow Learner in Science," *The American Biology Teacher* (March, 1966).

Barnard, J. Darrell. "What Can Science Contribute to the Liberal Education of All Children," *The Science Teacher* (November, 1965), pp. 24–26.

Bruner, Jerome. "Liberal Education for All Youth," *The Science Teacher* (November, 1965), pp. 19–21.

Cohen, Robert. "Individuality and Common Purpose: The Philosophy of Science," *The Science Teacher* (May, 1964).

Diederich, Paul B. "Components of the Scientific Attitude," *The Science Teacher* (February, 1967), pp. 23–24.

Fox, Fred. "Education and the Spirit of Science—The New Challenge," *The Science Teacher* (November, 1966), pp. 58–59.

Haney, Richard E. "The Development of Scientific Attitudes," *The Science Teacher* (December, 1964), pp. 33–35.

Hawkins, David. "Education and the Spirit of Science," *The Science Teacher* (September, 1966), pp. 18–20.

Kline, Morris. "The Liberal Education Values of Science," *The Science Teacher* (November, 1965).

Pauling, Linus. "The Social Responsibilities of Scientists and Science," *The Science Teacher* (May, 1966), pp. 14–18.

[18] Glenn T. Seaborg, "A Scientific Society—The Beginnings," in S. Rapport and H. Wright (eds.), *Science: Method and Meaning* (New York: Washington Square Press, 1963).

Roberts, Walter Orr. "Science, A Wellspring of Our Discontent," *The American Scholar* (Spring, 1967), pp. 246–60.

Shamos, Morris H. "Science and Common Sense," *The Science Teacher* (September, 1962).

Thelen, Herbert A. "The Triumph of 'Achievement Over Inquiry' in Education," *The Elementary School Journal*, Vol. 60, No. 4 (January, 1960), pp. 190–97.

Tyler, Ralph W. "Forces Redirecting Science Teaching," *The Science Teacher* (October, 1962).

Additional References (Books)

Butts, David P. (ed.). *Designs for Progress in Science Education*. Washington, D.C.: National Science Teachers Association, 1969.

Broudy, Harry S., B. Othanel Smith, and Joe R. Barnett. *Democracy and Excellence in American Secondary Education*. Chicago: Rand McNally & Co., 1964.

Cuban, Larry. *To Make a Difference: Teaching in the Inner City*. New York: The Macmillan Company, 1970.

Grobman, Arnold B. (ed.). *Social Implications of Biological Education*. Garden City, N.Y.: National Association of Biology Teachers, 1970.

Henry, Nelson B. (ed.). *Rethinking Science Education*. Chicago: University of Chicago Press, 1960.

Hurd, Paul DeHart. *New Directions in Teaching Secondary School Science*. Chicago: Rand McNally & Co., 1969.

Lee, Eugene C. *New Developments in Science Teaching*. Belmont, Calif.: Wadsworth Publishing Co., Inc., 1967.

Mager, Robert F. *Developing Attitude Toward Learning*. Palo Alto, Calif.: Fearon Publishers, Inc., 1968.

Novak, Joseph D. *The Improvement of Biology Teaching*. Indianapolis: The Bobbs-Merrill Co., 1970.

N.S.T.A. *Theory into Action: In Science Curriculum Development*. Washington, D.C.: National Science Teachers Association, 1964.

Schwab, Joseph J., and Paul F. Brandwein. *The Teaching of Science*. Cambridge, Mass.: Harvard University Press, 1962.

Washton, Nathan S. *Teaching Science Creatively in the Secondary Schools*. Philadelphia: W. B. Saunders Company, 1967.

a rationale for planning

In this chapter some basic elements and ideas of planning for instruction will be discussed. The chapter is intended to introduce you to the idea of planning. Later chapters will discuss many of the ideas in much more detail. The chapter will proceed from a discussion of some general ideas, through a discussion of the daily lesson plan, to a discussion of unit planning.

Planning can be defined as all the activities performed by teachers that are directed toward arranging conditions predicted capable of causing behavioral change in students. This broad definition includes every teacher act, from exhibiting interest in extracurricular activities to leading an extracurricular activity, from planning an entire science curriculum to designing a single lesson plan, and from designing a science facility to arranging furniture within a science laboratory. Though every teacher act cannot be preplanned, the teacher who diligently plans will usually be successful.

That planning must be evolutionary is the first and perhaps most important consideration. The "ideal" lesson is rarely the product of the initial planning session; it has generally evolved through a series of writing, evaluating, and rewriting cycles. Preparing a lesson plan is thus very similar to preparing programed instruction. Developmental testing or the process of trying out the lesson plan with many students, evaluating its success, rewriting, retrying, and re-evaluating, which is the essence of programmed instruction, is also the essence of good teacher planning.

Planning must be a continuous process. Beginning teachers are frequently told that if they work hard and develop a good set of lesson plans in their first year of teaching, planning will be easy in subsequent years. If experience provides nothing else, it should give the perceptive teacher an increased awareness of individual differences in the students. As this increased awareness of individual differences develops, the teacher should begin designing lesson plans to accommodate these individual differences. The teacher who attempts to utilize the same general lesson plan year after year will have one year of experience twenty times! The teacher who sees planning as an evolutionary process that is necessarily continuous will have a full twenty years of diverse experience. Which teacher will cause the greatest degree of change in the student? Which teacher will have the most student respect? Which teacher would *you* like to be?

Plans must be flexible. They are, at best, hypotheses. The teacher hypothesizes that if he arranges X conditions and uses Y strategy, the student will be able to perform a particular task (terminal behavior). The teacher must, at all times, be prepared to depart from his preplanned strategy if it is not causing change, or if a more productive means of proceeding becomes evident. The "ideal" lesson plan will consist of several branches or paths. The teacher using such a plan will ask questions and evaluate student responses and then use the information gained as criteria for selecting the path or branch to pursue. The ideal lesson plan thus resembles a highly branched program, but unlike the typical paper-and-pencil program, it need not be limited to what is on the printed page. The teacher can evaluate the manner in which the response is given as well as the response. And the teacher can combine branches and synthesize new branches whenever the alternatives do not produce the desired behavioral change.

Planning must consider the knowledge, attitudes, and skills of the students. If students do not have the necessary prerequisites, they will often be unable to assimilate the new material. A student cannot understand a principle unless the concepts subsumed by the principle are understood. Similarly, a student will not be able to solve a problem unless he understands the principles that are operative within the problem.

Planning must be evaluated. The teacher should determine the effectiveness of each lesson at its conclusion. The teacher must know whether he can begin the next lesson immediately, or whether some degree of instructional repetition is required. Evaluation at this point does not include a judgment of the lesson plan. It merely indicates the degree of success with the particular population at the particular time it was used. If the lesson was successful, a high percentage of students will be capable of the predicted performance. If the plan was not successful, it simply means that the teacher must design another strategy, or arrange different conditions. It does not mean that the day's effort was necessarily the result of poor instruction.

In spite of the fact that construction of the "perfect" lesson plan seems impossible, the process and the attempt to reach this goal can be the most exciting challenge of teaching. It might also be the most rewarding! Its prime importance is derived from the fact that it is a plan for action—your action—on a particular day with your students, which is designed to develop a specific set of terminal behaviors in these students.

The Daily Lesson Plan

The preparation of a lesson plan or teaching strategy for a single day differs from all other planning in that it involves hypothesizing a teaching behavior which will develop the desired terminal performances of a specific group of students in a given environmental setting. The syllabus, unit plan, text, and sourcebook are useful sources of information concerning what is available and which terminal behaviors should be developed. The classroom teacher is, however, the ultimate facilitator of the master plan, he must make it work in his classroom with his students.

Although anyone may be able to cause a considerable amount of behavioral change in a given set of students on a given day, such success is not necessarily tantamount to good instruction. Good instruction has *a past, a present*, and *a future*. It begins where the students are and provides them with the knowledge, attitudes, and skills they will need to operate within that context or similar contexts at some future date.

The fact that simply causing behavioral change is not enough emphasizes the fact that designing the daily lesson plan is the teacher's most important function. Because if what happens in the classroom on a given day does not contribute to the broad goals of the course, the day's instruction may be of little value to the students. Furthermore, a day is not just five hours of instruction. The number of student hours lost is the real issue. If you have 120 students, a "lost day" may easily mean that 120 hours are lost.

The lesson-plan format outlined below contains the minimum number of factors which must be considered when a lesson is being planned. Three of the five elements of lesson planning are discussed in greater detail on the pages which follow. A rationale for using specific performance objectives and a discussion of testing and teacher redirection are subjects of other chapters.

A Lesson-Plan Format

1. State objectives.
   a. General objective(s).
   b. Specific performances objective(s).
2. Hypothesize means to attain objectives.
   a. Brainstorm.
      (1) Outline all possible procedures.
      (2) Describe desired resources (man, materials, setting, and so on).
   b. Select.
      (1) Describe actual resources.
      (2) List criteria for strategy selection.
      (3) Select strategy (strategies).
3. Hypothesized implementation procedure.
   a. Approaching "mind capture."
   b. Development. $\Big\} N$
   c. Evaluation Sample.
4. Test items for evaluation.
5. Redirection: basically, a statement of
   a. How you will use the data collected in 3c and 4 to redirect your efforts.
   b. Other self-evaluation steps you will take.

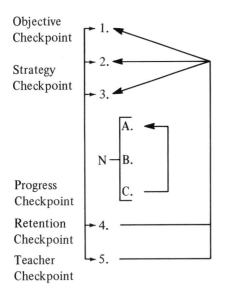

Objective Checkpoint

Strategy Checkpoint

Progress Checkpoint

Retention Checkpoint

Teacher Checkpoint

1. Are the objectives appropriate?

2. How many different ways could these objectives be taught? How can the best strategy or strategies be selected?

3. Are the students enjoying the lesson? Are the students able to answer your questions?

4. Was the information learned in the lesson retained until examination time?

5. How might I modify my teaching behavior to improve instruction?

Figure 4-1. Lesson-planning checkpoints.

This lesson-plan format was designed to outline five steps essential to good planning. These five steps outline the planning processes used by most teachers; however, you would probably never find a teacher proceeding systematically from 1 to 5. Each of the five steps can become a check or decision point, and if the teacher were to apply criteria rigorously at each point, he would become a more effective planner. Figure 4-1 illustrates the checkpoints and some questions which could be asked at each checkpoint.

Objectives

1. General objectives: Objectives stated in general terms which relate the topic to its past and future. The general objectives should relate the specific daily lesson to the unit.
2. Specific performance objectives: These objectives should state the hypothetical outcome of the planned instruction. Each objective should consist of three parts (assume that these objectives may be given to students).
   a. Situation, which describes the situation in which the student will be placed when his performance is being measured.
   b. Performance term, which is a measurable term which describes what the student should be able to do.
   c. Qualifying terms, which delimit performance, indicating the degree of sophistication or accuracy the student must attain for minimal acceptable performance.

HYPOTHESIZE MEANS TO ATTAIN OBJECTIVES

Although stating all the possible means of achieving the objectives may appear to be little more than an academic exercise, this step has at least two important functions. First, the process of stating all possible alternatives will frequently permit the teacher to select the best strategy or strategies. Second, if the first alternative does not cause the desired change in students, the teacher has a second alternative partially planned. (The need for additional supplies or equipment may eliminate the possibility of employing a given strategy in a given year. The hypothesized alternatives can form the basis for your future purchases.) Hence the process of stating all possibilities and selecting a strategy or strategies allows the teacher to discover what he can do in a given school setting and what he might be able to do if the setting were changed.

HYPOTHESIZED IMPLEMENTATION PROCEDURE

The division of the procedure into three segments is artificial. It is designed in this manner to focus attention on the teaching act as a tripartite function: motivation, cognition, evaluation. This is a simplified description of the teaching act; however, it does permit the teacher the opportunity to focus his attention on three teacher functions: motivating students, helping students learn, and evaluating his own and his student's success. This cycle may be repeated several times during a single period.

The approach is particularly important at the beginning of the period. A teacher who assumes that the bell signaling the beginning of the period simultaneously transforms his charges into little scientists will be quickly disillusioned. When the bell rings, the students may be anywhere. Even the ones who appear alert and attentive may have their thoughts focused on a safari in deepest Africa, the Friday night dance, or a preschool family feud. Focusing the students' attention on the lesson to be taught is the first objective of each teaching situation. Woodburn and Obourn refer to this as "mind capture."[1] The most effective means of establishing mind capture is to design an attention-getting situation which is interesting, dramatic, and relevant to the student's background. Short demonstrations containing a discrepant event, provocative statements, and divergent questions are frequently effective mind-capture devices.

The success of the approach may be measured by observing the transition from the dramatic mind-capture event to the main body of the day's lesson. If after the first few exciting minutes the lesson appears to fall flat, you will know that the approach was not effective and you will have to reapproach the topic. Though the real difficulty may lie in development, the lack of student involvement and enthusiasm indicates a need to re-establish mind capture.

Once the students are involved in the actual process of learning something that *they* feel is important, they will generally want to continue learning. The process of learning frequently motivates a desire for more learning; however, developing this desire to learn is probably a function of student interest. If the material is meaningful to the student, he will develop his own motivation for learning. This focuses the teacher's function to one of making instruction meaningful to the students. This does not mean that it is the teacher's job to teach only interesting things. *It is the teacher's job to make those things which must be taught interesting.*

The development section of the lesson plan should contain a logical presentation of ideas. The actual material to be taught should be studied and the teacher should hypothesize his procedure. At times a deductive approach centering on applying a generalization to a specific area of concern may seem

---

[1] John Woodburn and Ellsworth S. Obourn, *Teaching the Pursuit of Science* (New York: Macmillan, 1965), 285 pp.

most appropriate. At other times approaching the generalization inductively by examining specific situations and developing the generalization may seem most appropriate. Which is best, in general? The two approaches cannot be evaluated in this manner. Those specific ideas which can be treated most effectively by deductive processes should be explored deductively. Similarly, ideas and problem situations which can be explored most effectively, through induction, should be so treated. Science is based on inductive and deductive processes.[2] Therefore, if a science course is to reflect accurately the nature of science, the teacher must plan to involve students in both inductive and deductive processes.

The decision to proceed either inductively or deductively is the first step in structuring the daily lesson. Organizing the sequence of inductive or deductive steps and/or leaps which will direct the student toward the desired terminal behavior is the biggest challenge. Structuring the material is extremely important. The following example illustrates the value of structuring material.

Examine the following list of words and remember them in order. Time yourself.

correspond	make	to
chaotic	to	system
is	a	uniform
diversity	the	of
experience	sense	thought
attempt	our	of
science	the	logically

Perhaps you did not even care to tackle a task which appeared ridiculous, and if you did proceed, you probably did not find the task either interesting or enjoyable. If structure is added or you are directed to arrange the words in a sequence (structure) prior to remembering them, chances are that the job would become far more exciting and certainly much easier. Re-examine the words as they were originally structured and memorize them. Time yourself.

Science is the attempt to make the chaotic diversity of our sense experience correspond to a logically uniform system of thought.[3]

Unstructured lessons cause as much chaos as scrambling Einstein's

[2] James T. Robinson, *The Nature of Science and Science Teaching* (Belmont, Calif.: Wadsworth, 1968), 149 pp.

[3] Albert Einstein, "Considerations Concerning the Fundamentals of Theoretical Physics," *Science*, Vol. 9 (1940), p. 487.

definition of science. The teacher interested in avoiding the scrambled confusion must carefully structure each lesson in a meaningful manner.

The success of any lesson is determined by the ability of the students to demonstrate the behavior specified in the performance objective, which is referred to as the terminal behavior. Questioning students or providing them with a task or problem to solve is perhaps the easiest way to determine if the students possess the desired terminal behavior. Hence, questions should be asked throughout the period at appropriate points and at the end, when total terminal behaviors can be assessed.

Ending a lesson with the time-worn summary, "Today we have learned ta, da, ta, da, fa, da," is not only improper, but grossly inaccurate. It is inaccurate in that without attempting some sort of measurement it is impossible to estimate what "we" have learned. It is improper in that it will tend to raise the anxiety level of the students who have not learned the desired material. Anxiety will tend to force the students to react in a negative manner or attempt to incorporate the material on a very low and highly perishable level.[4]

Questions with answers that demonstrate terminal performance should be asked of key individuals at the end of each lesson. This procedure is particularly necessary if the next lesson is based on knowledge, skills, or attitudes developed during the period. If terminal behavior on lesson 1 is the necessary entry behavior for lesson 2, proceeding to lesson 2 without measuring the success of lesson 1 may be a waste of time.

Unit Plans

The daily lesson plan is the ultimate design for action on a given day in a given classroom. It is a small piece of a very large plan called a unit plan. Unit plans may consist of lesson plans that are arranged together to teach the students the basic facts and principles subsumed by a big idea. Or the unit plan may be a structured outline which describes the student performances available to guide students toward understanding of big ideas. The units included in the texts listed below define what is meant by the term *big idea.*

    1. B.S.C.S., *Biological Science: Molecules to Man* (Boston: Houghton-Mifflin, 1968), 840 pp.

       Unit One. Biology: The Interaction of Facts and Ideas.

       Unit Two. Evolution of Life Processes.

---

[4] Walter Waetjen, "Learning and Motivation: Implications for the Teaching of Science," *The Science Teacher* (May, 1965).

Unit Three. The Evolution of the Cell.

Unit Four. Multicellular Organisms: New Individuals.

Unit Five. Multicellular Organisms: Genetic Continuity.

Unit Six. Multicellular Organisms: Energy Utilization.

Unit Seven. Unifying Systems.

Unit Eight. Higher Levels of Organization.

2. B.S.C.S., *High School Biology* (Chicago: Rand McNally, 1968), 823 pp.

Section One. The World of Life: The Biosphere.

Section Two. Diversity Among Living Things.

Section Three. Patterns in the Biosphere.

Section Four. Within the Individual Organism.

Section Five. Continuity of the Biosphere.

Section Six. Man and the Biosphere.

3. F. Albert Cotton and Lawrence Lynch, *Chemistry: An Investigative Approach* (Boston: Houghton Mifflin, 1968), 660 pp.

Unit One. From Questions to Knowledge.

Unit Two. Atoms and Molecules: Building Blocks of Matter.

Unit Three. The Dynamics of Chemistry.

Unit Four. Families of Elements.

Unit Five. Neighboring Elements.

Unit Six. The Universe of Chemistry.

The unit plan can be regarded as a package of hypothesized strategies designed to assist the teacher. It may suggest alternative routes. For example, assume that the following diagram is a unit which proceeds from an overview of a big idea through several related and subsumed facts and principles and ends by converging on student "mastery" of the idea suggested at the beginning. Each of the dots represents a teaching strategy or lesson plan for a single day, or in some cases, for two or three days. All of the strategies on the horizontal lines are designed to get at the same fact or principle. The teacher may begin by selecting a route from beginning to end which he feels will cause the desired degree of learning. As he proceeds through the unit, he may quiz students (oral and/or paper quizzes) to determine that the desired learning has occurred. By constantly questioning the students he can discover when additional work in a given area is desirable or he may involve some students in different activities.

The diagram illustrates the movement of a class through a unit. In this situation only a few strategies of all those possible were used. It is also evident that the teacher did not have the entire class doing the same thing

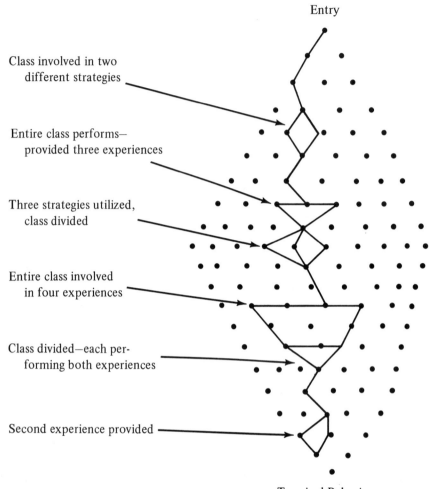

Figure 4-2.   Resources and class activities throughout a unit.

each day. The confused pattern is typical. Anyone who assumes that a class will move through a unit along a neat path as represented by the broken line usually discovers the students closer to entry behavior than desired terminal behavior when the unit test is administered.

The beginning teacher should begin with an outline of the unit. As he proceeds from year to year, he should continue developing alternate strategies for his unit. Whenever one strategy fails, he should design another. However, he cannot be too hasty about discarding the strategy which did not work with *X* pupils during *Y* year; it may be the "best" strategy for the next year.

Evaluation

Evaluation is certainly not the most important teacher activity, but without evaluation instructional effectiveness cannot be ascertained. Teaching strategies should certainly be evaluated as rigorously as student performance. The evaluation of a teaching strategy should begin with a pretrial examination of the elements of the strategy. Ultimate evaluation of the strategy can only be ascertained by observing and carefully evaluating student performances resulting from the strategy. The checklist can be used for the pretrial examination.

CHECKLIST FOR THE PRETRIAL EVALUATION OF A LESSON PLAN

_____ 1. Does the strategy fit in at this particular point in the unit? Does it have a *past*, a *present*, and a *future*?
    a. Do the students have the prerequisite knowledge, skills, and attitudes (past)?
    b. Is the strategy economical in terms of time and energy (present)?
    c. Will the strategy provide students with the power they need for the next strategy (future)?

_____ 2. Are the terminal performances stated in measurable terms?

_____ 3. Will the approach establish mind capture?

_____ 4. Is the development sequential and logically constructed, proceeding from either general to specific or specific to general?

_____ 5. Will the teacher's questions determine the degree of mastery attained by the students?

_____ 6. Is the assignment clearly stated and geared to the ability of the students?

_____ 7. Are references cited appropriate for the student population?

_____ 8. Have the available teacher aids, including films, filmstrips, and programmed material, been included?

_____ 9. Are the equipment and supplies available?

_____ 10. Is there a planned evaluation of
    a. Your performance.
    b. Your student's performance.

PROBLEMS

1. How would you answer the following statements?
    a. Only beginning teachers need to make lesson plans!
    b. Teachers who prepare lesson plans drag their students through a lesson instead of leading them!
    c. Lesson planning makes teachers rigid!

2. Outline a plan that you believe would permit you to become an effective planner.

Additional References

Banathy, Bella H. *Instructional Systems.* Palo Alto, Calif.: Fearon Publishing, Inc., 1968.

Bloom, B. S., A. Davis, and R. Hess. *Compensatory Education for Cultural Deprivation.* New York: Holt, Rinehart & Winston, 1965.

Bremner, Jean. *Teaching Biology.* New York: St. Martin's Press, 1967.

Haney, John B., and Eldon J. Ullmer. *Educational Media and the Teacher.* Dubuque, Iowa: William C. Brown Company, Publishers, 1970.

Harding, Delma, Roger P. Volker, and David L. Fagle. *Creative Biology Teaching.* Ames: Iowa State University Press, 1969.

Lacey, Archie L. *Guide to Science Teaching.* Belmont, Calif.: Wadsworth Publishing Company, 1966.

Lesser, David L. "Systematic Planning: An Answer to Educational Dilemmas," *The Science Teacher* (May, 1969).

Pfeiffer, John. *New Look at Education: Systems Analysis in our Schools and Colleges.* New York: Odyssey Press, 1968.

Popham, W. James. *Establishing Instructional Goals.* Englewood Cliffs, N.J.: Prentice-Hall, Inc., 1970.

Popham, W. James, and Eva L. Baker. *Planning an Instructional Sequence.* Englewood Cliffs, N.J.: Prentice-Hall, Inc., 1970.

Popham, W. James, and Eva L. Baker. *Systematic Instruction.* Englewood Cliffs, N.J.: Prentice-Hall, Inc., 1970.

Smith, Karl U., and Margaret Foltz Smith. *Cybernetic Principles of Learning and Educational Design.* New York: Holt, Rinehart and Winston, Inc., 1966.

Sund, Robert B., and Leslie W. Trowbridge. *Teaching Science by Inquiry in the Secondary School.* Columbus, Ohio: Charles E. Merrill Publishing Company, 1967.

Thurber, Walter A., and Alfred T. Collette. *Teaching Science in Today's Secondary Schools*, 3rd ed. Boston: Allyn & Bacon, 1968.

Torrance, E. Paul. *Encouraging Creativity in the Classroom.* Dubuque, Iowa: William C. Brown Company, Publishers, 1970.

Voss, Burton E., and Stanley B. Brown. *Biology as Inquiry: A Book of Teaching Methods.* St. Louis, Mo.: The C. V. Mosby Co., 1968.

specific performance objectives

Performance or behavioral objectives are measurable statements of hypothesized postinstructional student behavior. The current emphasis on specifying performances or behaviors in specific measurable terms is based on two assumptions, each with merit but neither with guarantees of significantly improved education. First, it is assumed that when students are told exactly what they are expected to learn, more learning will occur. Second, it is assumed that when teachers decide specifically what is to be taught, they will become more proficient in designing their instruction. That is, teachers will (1) tend to break content to be taught into smaller, more meaningful pieces, (2) be more proficient at arranging the smaller pieces into logical instructional sequences, (3) develop greater expertise in determining the performance capabilities of their students, and (4) become more competent in selecting the methods and media of instruction.

The first assumption, that students will learn more if they know precisely what they are expected to learn, is a safe assumption to make. However, additional achievement only becomes noteworthy when it provides the student additional power (attitude + knowledge + skill) to work in the area being studied and in related areas. If the added achievement does not contribute to the future success of the individual, the fact that it has been achieved is not important.

The second assumption also deserves a closer look. Breaking content into smaller pieces and constructing logical hierarchies may significantly improve education. However, the pieces and the hierarchies must be examined carefully. Good instruction has a past, a present, and most particularly, a future. Good instruction begins where the students are. It provides meaningful experience and it prepares the student for additional experience. The process of breaking content into smaller pieces and arranging it in logical hierarchies does not necessarily guarantee excellent instruction, even when excellent teachers are involved. Each piece and each hierarchy must be examined in terms of the criteria of good instruction and then tested with the student population.

The logical hierarchies developed must be tested in the classroom. Although the teacher may easily become an expert on which pieces of content to include, arranging these pieces of content for student consumption is another matter. What may constitute a logical hierarchy to a teacher, or even a population of teachers, may be very illogical for some, and possibly the majority of, students.

What Are Performance Objectives?

Performance or behavioral objectives are objectives which state in measurable terms a specific performance or behavior that a student should be able to demonstrate as a result of the instruction provided. Performance objectives are statements which consist of three elements—terms which describe the testing situation, measurable performance terms, and qualifying terms which describe the level of sophistication deemed acceptable.

The Situation

The situation portion of the performance objective should indicate what the student will be given when his performance is being measured. It may describe the physical environment, materials, or information provided the student. Examine the examples:

1. Given a diagram of a "typical" cell.
2. Given a deep well slide, cover slip, and culture of bacteria.
3. Given access to high-interest science and science fiction books.
4. Given a problem situation involving force, mass, and acceleration.
5. Given a problem situation in an area new to the student.

Using *given* to initiate each phase is not necessary; however, it facilitates writing by focusing the writer's mind on what he plans to provide the student when his performance is being measured.

The Performance Term

Objectives frequently contain words like *know, understand, really understand*, and *appreciate*. These unmeasurable terms provide very little direction for either the teacher or the student. Assume that you are given the following objective for a day of instruction: "The student should know the recapitulation theory." Your instruction and the student's performance would be determined by your definition of the word *know*. If you decide that knowing only implies the ability to repeat the theory, your instruction could involve very little planning or effort. You might simply have the students memorize the terse terms of Ernst Hackel, "Ontogeny recapitulates phylogeny." Students would fulfill the performance requirement by simply restating the three words in response to the question, "What is the recapitulation theory?"

I doubt if anyone would agree that a student saying "Ontogeny recapitulates phylogeny" really knows the recapitulation theory. However, a student could claim that the three little words are a correct answer to the question. If instruction and measurement are to be concise, terms like to *know, understand*, and *appreciate* must be replaced by measurable performance terms. The following illustrations could all be performances subsumed by the original objective. The student should be able to

1. *Define* the recapitulation theory in his own words.
2. *Describe* situations in which the recapitulation theory appears to have been operative.
3. *List* possible exceptions to the recapitulation theory.
4. *Describe* evidence supporting the recapitulation theory.
5. *Compare* and *contrast* the recapitulation theory to the biogenetic law.
6. *Design* an experiment to test the recapitulation theory.

Listing these performances clearly delimits instruction and student performance. If you return to the original assumption that students will do better when they know exactly what is expected of them, you will probably have to conclude that the students given the six objectives will do more than the students given the objective containing the unmeasurable term *know*. The six performances cited are only a few examples; many more can be developed. The following lists of measurable performance terms give you some additional examples:

SOME ACTION VERBS FOR COGNITIVE OBJECTIVES

identify	apply	measure
distinguish	demonstrate	write
construct	interpret	recite
name	extrapolate	differentiate
order	state	solve
describe	translate	list
compare	construct	contrast
classify	calculate	transfer
design	synthesize	analyze
evaluate		

SOME ACTION VERBS FOR AFFECTIVE OBJECTIVES

selects	pursues	evaluates
participates	joins	tests
reads	examines	delays
gathers	synthesizes	qualities
organizes	questions	designs
visits	doubts	adapts
investigates	uses	supports
offers	repeats	revises
proposes	considers	undertakes
rejects	analyzes	challenges
consults	criticizes	seeks

SOME QUALIFYING ADVERBS FOR AFFECTIVE VERBS

individually	habitually	frequently
willingly	consistently	attentively
enthusiastically		

The following examples of performances are extensions of the situations stated earlier. The performance portion of the objective is in italics.

1. Given a diagram of a cell, *the student should be able to label its major structures.*
2. Given a deep well slide, cover slip, and culture of bacteria, *the student should be able to prepare a hanging drop slide and, with the aid of a microscope, locate the bacteria suspended in the drop.*
3. Given access to high-interest science and science fiction books, *the student should utilize some of his free time to read the books and prepare a report on their contents.*

4. Given a problem situation involving force, mass, and acceleration, *the student should be able to analyze the problem and write an explanation.*

5. Given a problem situation in an area new to the student, *the student should be able to construct hypotheses and design experimental plan(s) which may lead to a solution to the problem.*

The Qualifying Terms

Though a measurable performance term is present, the performance needs additional qualifying to specify the degree of sophistication, skill, or time defined as acceptable performance. Qualifying performances can be the most challenging and tentative aspect of writing performance objectives. The challenge results from the fact that qualifying terms must reflect both student potential and the type of instruction provided. If the qualifying terms do not reflect these two aspects, the possibility that students will achieve the desired performance is doubtful. The tentativeness results from the constant need for revision. The first two elements of a performance objective may be retained year after year. You may have to change the qualifying terms every year. Examine the qualifying terms added to the objectives developed:

1. Given a diagram of a "typical" cell, the student should be able to label its major structures. Acceptable performance includes correct labeling of eight of the following structures: cell membrane, mitochondria, endoplasmic reticulum, nucleus, nucleolus, centrosomes, lysosome, golgi body, nuclear membrane, cytoplasm, and pinocytic vesicle.

2. Given a deep well slide, cover slip, and culture of bacteria, the student should be able to prepare a hanging drop slide and, with the aid of a microscope, locate the bacteria suspended in the drop. Acceptable performance includes preparing a hanging drop which will not fall off and locating the bacteria within five minutes.

3. Given access to high-interest science and science fiction books, the student should utilize some of his free time to read the books and prepare a report on their contents. Acceptable performance includes reading one book each semester.

4. Given a problem situation involving force, mass, and acceleration, the student should be able to analyze the problem and write an explanation. Acceptable performance includes identifying the concepts within the problem and explaining the problem in terms of the concepts.

5. Given a problem situation in an area new to the student, the student should be able to construct hypotheses and design experimental plan(s) which may lead to a solution to the problem. Acceptable performance includes synthesizing two relevant hypotheses and two experimental designs.

Discussion Questions

1. In your opinion what are the major pitfalls in preparing performance objectives?
2. How will you avoid the pitfalls you specified? (Assume that you cannot avoid performance objectives.)
3. How will you determine if a performance objective has integrity and is really worth teaching?
4. What is the relationship between performance objectives and accountability?
5. Should teachers be accountable? To whom?

Additional References

Armstrong, Robert J., Terry D. Kramer, and E. Wayne Roberson. *Developing and Writing Behavioral Objectives*. Tucson, Ariz.: Educational Innovators Press, Inc., 1968.

Ebenson, Thorwald. "Writing Instructional Objectives," *Phi Delta Kappan* (January, 1968).

Eiss, Albert F., and Mary Blatt Harbeck. *Behavioral Objectives in the Affective Domain*. Washington, D.C.: National Science Teachers Association, 1969.

Gronlund, Norman E. *Stating Behavioral Objectives for Classroom Instruction*. New York: The Macmillan Company, 1970.

Kurtz, Edwin B. "Help Stamp Out Non-behavioral Objectives," *The Science Teacher* (March, 1968).

Mager, Robert F. *Preparing Instructional Objectives*. Palo Alto, Calif.: Fearon Publishers, 1962.

Popham, W. James, and Eva L. Backer. *Establishing Instructional Goals*. Englewood Cliffs, N.J.: Prentice-Hall, Inc., 1970.

Popham, W. James, et al. *Instructional Objectives*, American Educational Research Association Monograph. Chicago: Rand McNally & Co., 1969.

group teaching strategies

Teaching strategies that can be used with groups of students are discussed in this chapter. No attempt is made to indicate how and when to work with a group, or even how many students constitute a group. There is a fair amount of evidence that can be interpreted to indicate that group instruction will continue as an important instructional strategy even when instruction is completely individualized. There is also evidence which can be interpreted to mean that, at least today, the greatest emphasis should be placed on designing instruction for individuals rather than for groups of students. As the classroom teacher, you must decide when to assemble your entire class for group instruction and when to give your full attention to smaller groups or individual students. The authors hope that this chapter, which deals with group strategies, and chapters dealing with individualized instruction will help prepare you to make decisions on the strategy most appropriate at a specific time for your students.

Teaching strategies are usually formulated in an attempt to move a student from point A on a continuum to point B on a continuum.

$$A \xrightarrow{\text{Strategy}} B$$

When this idea is expressed as in the diagram, it appears simple; however, the subtle complexities unnerve the best teachers. We must ask immediately,

1. What is point A?
2. What is the terminal point B?
3. What difficulties must the students overcome in moving from A to B?
4. How can these difficulties be overcome?
5. Which strategy is the most efficient?

Point A represents the initial prestrategy position of the student; that is, the state in which the student exists before he masters the knowledge, skills, and attitudes defined as point B. Because students, even homogeneously grouped students, vary extensively in aptitude, intelligence, and experience, determining exactly where your instruction should begin (point A) is exceedingly difficult. The only practical solution to the problem is to design instruction which will lead all students to the necessary entry behavior (point A) before attempting to move them to the terminal point B.

Consider this analogy. In a baseball game a batter hits a single and advances safely to first base, which we could define as point A. The ultimate goal is to advance the runner around all bases to home plate. The immediate objective entails getting the runner to second base, which could be defined as point B.

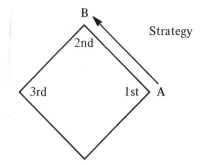

Figure 6-1.   Baseball–instruction analogy.

In the classroom some of the students fail to get to first base; others trip and fall turning a scratch single into an easy out; and some run completely past the base and turn the wrong way.

Continue studying the analogy by considering the difficulties which must be overcome to get the runner from state A on first to state B on second.

1. Who is the runner?

2. How rough is the field?

3. Will the team support the runner?

4. Will the coaches support the runner?

5. Is the total game situation, including the umpires, conducive to playing good baseball?

1. Who is the learner? (What individual abilities does he possess?)

2. Is the transition between A and B smooth, or are large leaps necessary?

3. Do his peers value learning?

4. Does the teacher encourage individual initiative?

5. Is the entire learning situation conducive to learning?

When all the difficulties are defined, the next problem is discovering ways and means of overcoming them. In the classroom, as in baseball (and for that matter, in life), success as a problem solver will be related to the number of strategies devised for attacking the problem. A baseball manager with a slow runner on first and the club's weakest batter at the plate must implement another strategy very quickly. The teacher, similarly, must examine all the strategies present and select that strategy best suited for the situation. The strategy that is most successful in moving the student from A to B is the most efficient, but it is only as efficient as it is economical. If the batter is only advanced to second and no farther, a run will not be scored. By *economical* it is implied not only that the student must be moved to the next state, but that the strategy will confer upon the student greater power, thereby enhancing his chances of continuing along the sequence referred to as the continuum.

Assume that you are teaching twenty-five individuals the principle involved in a neutralization reaction:

$$\text{Acid} + \text{Base} \rightleftharpoons \text{Salt} + \text{Water}$$

What is student state A? The obvious answer is that state A exists when the student does not "know" that if you mix an acid and a base you will get a salt + water. In reality, we are defining state A as not being at state B because we really have not defined exactly what it is that the student does not know. If we attempted to define state A, we might possibly discover that some students do not know what acids are, that others are confused by the word *base*, that some feel that all salt is NaCl, and that still others believe that all chemical reactions result in explosions. After defining state A as a vast array of individual differences extending from the ridiculous to the sublime, what will you do? What strategy or treatment will you design? How will you manage to move the ridiculous toward the sublime and the sublime to new heights within the defined confines of the instructional period? Consider briefly two broader aspects, instructional theory and the spirit of science.

Teaching Strategies and Instructional Theory

According to Bruner[1] a theory of instruction should consider four major features. These are predisposition, structure, sequence, and consequence. The following guidelines relate these elements to teaching strategies.

Teaching strategies should develop the individual's predisposition to learning. Kessen[2] indicates that evidence has begun to accumulate that supports the skillful variation of environmental uncertainty as a means of increasing a student's tendencies to search for more information, to retain, to understand, to transfer to new situations, and to recognize an achieved problem solution. He indicates that those properties of external stimulation which function to develop the intrinsic predisposition to change are customarily covered by such words as *novelty, change, surprisingness, complexity, incongruity, ambiguity*, and *lack of clarity*. To Kessen, developing a predisposition to learn would involve establishing an optimal amount of uncertainty which would cause the individual to enter into those activities described as learning. Remember, you cannot "learn" a student anything. Learning is something that the individual must do for himself.

An instructional theory should be both *prescriptive* and *normative*. It is *prescriptive* in the sense that it sets forth rules concerning the most effective means of developing a student's knowledge, skills, and attitudes. It is *normative* in the sense that it establishes criteria and states conditions for meeting them.

Second, teaching strategies should be structured so that the information provided can be grasped readily by the learner. The information provided through instruction should confer upon the student an increasing ability to simplify information, generate new propositions, and manipulate the body of knowledge he already possesses.

Third, teaching strategies should be sequenced in the most effective manner. Though principles of antecedence have frequently hindered curric-

---

[1] Jerome Bruner, *Toward a Theory of Instruction* (Cambridge, Mass.: Harvard University Press, 1966), 176 pp.

[2] William Kessen, "The Strategy of Instruction," in Jerome Bruner, ed., *Learning About Learning* (Washington, D.C.: U.S. Department of Health, Education and Welfare, 1966), pp. 98–104.

ulum construction, they cannot be ignored. Consider the neutralization reaction mentioned earlier.

$$\text{Acid} + \text{Base} \rightleftharpoons \text{Salt} + \text{Water}$$

A preschool-age child could be taught to regurgitate the words of this reaction. Regurgitating the statement would not indicate anything other than that the student could successfully repeat the words in a prescribed sequence. If teaching this principle is an objective, the information must be sequenced effectively. The student must be able to define acids, bases, salts, water, and, at least roughly, chemical reaction. Once he has knowledge of the nature of the reactants and the idea of chemical change through chemical reactions, he will be able to comprehend the nature of the reaction, apply the principle in new situations, analyze situations in which the reaction occurs, and hypothesize the outcome of similar reactions. If instructional sequence is ignored, the power associated with proper sequencing will not be realized by the students, and because the knowledge does not provide power, it will probably be highly perishable.

Finally, teaching strategies should be designed with a proper perspective of rewards and punishments. Initially, extrinsic teacher-provided rewards may necessarily predominate. If, however, the instructor establishes a predisposition to learning through effective sequencing and structuring, the students will tend to become self-energized. The self-energized child will find solving a complex problem intrinsically rewarding.

The Spirit of Science

The teacher who views his function as simply purveying large quantities of factual information will not be justly serving his students or science. Science is more than content! Science is a neatly interwoven schema consisting of content, process, and values. Teaching which does not emphasize all three dimensions of science fails to place it in its proper perspective and fails to represent science honestly.

Science curricula have been developed which emphasize both the processes and content of science. Values have not been ignored, but their treatment has been incidental. As teachers, we could promote the understanding of the values which underlie all science by emphasizing the seven values discussed by the Educational Policies Commission.[3] These are

[3] Educational Policies Commission, *Education and the Spirit of Science* (Washington, D.C.: National Education Association, 1966), 27 pp.

1. Longing to know and understand.
2. Questioning of all things.
3. Search for data and their meaning.
4. Demand for verification.
5. Respect for logic.
6. Consideration of premises.
7. Consideration of consequences.

Like all values, these are only guidelines. It would be difficult to design instruction which would emphasize all seven of these values on any given day. However, any instruction which does not emphasize at least one of the values should be questioned.

Teaching Strategies

Strategies used by teachers to move the student from *A* to *B* are many and varied. Some strategies are more effective than others, but there is no single strategy most effective with all students and all subject matter. It is necessary to select the best strategy for the particular student population.

The simple fact that some strategies are better than others and that no one strategy is best for all situations should encourage the teacher to utilize a variety of strategies. Variety should not be arranged simply for its own sake. The variety of strategies utilized should be selected on the basis of their effectiveness with a particular population of students and the particular subject matter. A description and discussion follows of several different teaching strategies which have been effective. In the discussion of each strategy an attempt will be made to describe what the teacher does, what the student is supposed to do, and the evident strengths and weaknesses of the strategy. The strengths and weaknesses should be given careful attention. A particular strength can hinder rather than help and weaknesses can often be overcome.

The Lecture Method

In recent years the lecture method has received more criticism than any teaching strategy, yet it continues to be used extensively. Its extensive use is probably a function of the teacher's eager desire to convey his vast knowledge in as direct a manner as possible and of the willingness of teachers to equate coverage with teaching. Its use may also be attributed to a general feeling that lecture material is very easy to prepare.

The lecture is a monologue arranged for presentation by the lecturer in a manner the lecturer deems appropriate. The topics discussed within the lecture should be arranged in some logical structure and sequenced in an economical manner. The lecturer assumes that the student is capable of receiving the material as presented, associating it with past experience and internally arranging it in a manner which will permit instant recall at some future moment.

The lecture is undoubtedly one of the most efficient means of purveying large quantities of information in short periods of time. If the assumptions concerning what a student is capable of doing during a lecture period were acceptable, it would undoubtedly be the major, or perhaps only, teaching strategy necessary. However, lecturers are often incapable of arranging and presenting material in a manner most students can assimilate. In addition, students are not consistently capable of receiving, rearranging, storing, and recalling information presented to them via this mode of instruction. It is obvious that anyone using this strategy makes assumptions about his audience which probably are not true.

ADVANTAGES

1. Efficient means of distributing a vast amount of knowledge.

DISADVANTAGE

1. Most students are not consistently capable of assimilating and internalizing material presented in this manner.
2. Lack of feedback. The straight lecture does not give the lecturer an opportunity to evaluate student progress during the period.
3. Extensive preparation time is usually required. The material presented, if it is to be meaningful to the student, must attract the student's attention and then move him through a sequence of logically and/or psychologically arranged steps toward the desired terminal behavior. The success of the lecture must be measured in terms of both its ability to attract attention and its ability to move the students toward the new terminal behavior.

Case Analysis and Case History

The case analysis and case history strategies are modified lecture–discussion techniques which permit the students to enter into the process called inquiry. The strategy basically involves providing the students with data and forcing them to draw conclusions from it. When the names of the original researchers are included and/or an attempt is made to place the student in the context of the original research, the strategy is called a case history.

The teacher planning to utilize this strategy begins by collecting information relative to a specific scientific idea. The information is then arranged chronologically for presentation to the student. The teacher in the classroom gives the students the data from a given experiment and asks the students to draw conclusions from the information given. The student is told that he can only use the information provided.

The student actively participates in this strategy by attempting to draw conclusions from stated data, and in some cases he must attempt to place himself in the context of the original discoverers. As the student proceeds from one case to another, he is directed through discovery processes which may be similar to those of the original researchers. In a well-developed case analysis or history, the student is also led up nonproductive paths to discover negative data and/or data which do not contribute to a better definition of the problem or idea being investigated.

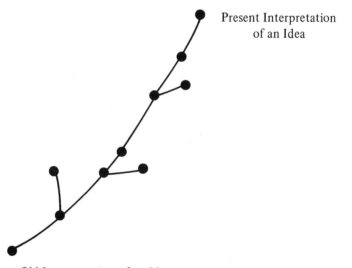

Present Interpretation
of an Idea

Old Interpretation of an Idea

Figure 6-2. Diagram of a case analysis. The circles represent experimental evidence that is provided. The nonproductive paths are represented by the short projections from the main line.

ADVANTAGES

1. The student can participate actively as a member of a class group or an individual.
2. The emphasis is placed upon the manipulation of data and ideas rather than simply collecting data or remembering conclusions.

3. The deductive thought processes involved honestly represent science.
4. Research indicates this strategy can influence the student's attitude toward science in a very positive manner.[4]

DISADVANTAGES

1. The teacher may have to construct many of the case analyses himself. Though there are a few case histories developed for use in the secondary school, many more are needed. *The History of Science Cases* developed by Leo E. Klopfer[5] and Joseph Schwab's "Invitations to Enquiry"[6] are two good examples of these hard-to-find materials.
2. Negative instances and examples of nonproductive research are not always reported in the literature. Hence, it may frequently be necessary to insert an hypothetical negative instance at appropriate positions. (The optimal number of negative instances is not known.)

Demonstration

A demonstration can be defined as simply showing something to another person or group. In science instruction this strategy typically involves showing students apparatus they are to use, illustrating a technique, performing an "experiment" which is either too dangerous or too expensive for individual student use, or establishing a discrepant event.[7]

The first three uses of the demonstration can be performed in a relatively mechanical manner and frequently fail to arouse the interest of the students unless the instructor makes an effort to involve students. Student involvement is planned when a discrepant event is illustrated. A teacher using a discrepant event encourages the student to advance an hypothesis concerning a phenomenon with which the student is relatively familiar. In other words, the predictions made by the student should be based on factual information he knows. The teacher then acts by arranging the conditions in such a way that the expected does not occur, and then leads the students into a discussion of other factors that may be involved. The students may be asked to suggest

---

[4] Leopold E. Klopfer and William W. Cooley, "The History of Science Cases for High Schools in the Development of Student Understanding of Science and Scientists," A Report of the HOSC Instruction Project, *Journal of Research in Science Teaching*, Vol. I, Issue I (1963).

[5] Leo E. Klopfer, *History of Science Cases* (Chicago: Science Research Associates, 1966).

[6] Joseph Schwab, *Biology Teacher's Handbook* (New York: Wiley, 1963).

[7] A discrepant event is an event that a student cannot predict in spite of the fact that he knows several facts which should explain what should occur. For example, a student who knows about gravity would predict that if you dropped a ball it would fall. If instead the ball moved upward, you would have established a discrepant event.

experiments which could be performed to determine which of the newly suggested factors may be responsible for the discrepant event. For example, a teacher just finishing a discussion of gravity may use the following demonstration.

1. Select two test tubes, one of which barely fits into the other.
2. Fill the larger test tube with water and insert the smaller test tube until it displaces a quantity of water greater than its own mass.

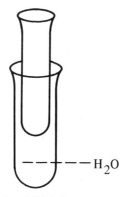

Figure 6-3.   Initial demonstration set-up.

3. Ask the students the following questions:
   a. If I hold the larger test tube and turn the system upside down, what *might* happen to the smaller test tube? (Solicit all possibilities.)
   b. What do you think will happen? Why?
4. Perform the demonstration. (The smaller, inner test tube will typically move up into the larger tube, replacing the water which drips out.)

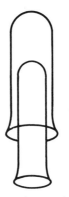

Figure 6-4.   Inverted test tube–water system.

5. Then ask,
    c. Why did the inner tube not fall out as we had predicted?
    d. Which reasons seem to be the best?
    e. How could we discover which factors are operating to cause the effect we noted?

The preceding example illustrates how a demonstration can be used to establish inquiry. Inquiry demonstrating need not be limited to situations involving discrepant events. The discrepant event may optimize the opportunity to involve a group of students actively in problem-solving activities. The success of a demonstration is determined by its ability to involve the students actively in the work that is to follow. If the demonstration has only a present and does not open new doors for exploration, it has little value.

After seeing a demonstration the student should be able to analyze the events and hypothesize reasonable conclusions. Inasmuch as this is a teacher-directed activity, the teacher must arrange to permit student involvement.

ADVANTAGES

1. The discrepant-event approach provides individuals an opportunity to participate in group problem-solving activities.
2. The discrepant-event strategy can afford an excellent means of introducing or approaching a new topic.
3. Phenomena too expensive or dangerous for laboratory work can be illustrated.

DISADVANTAGES

1. Student participation may be limited to a few of the most verbal children.
2. The phenomena demonstrated may not be seen equally well by all members of the class.
3. The teacher may use too much direct influence and illustrate teacher problem solving rather than involving pupils in problem-solving situations.

Laboratory

The footnotes to a statement declaring that the "essence of science can only be discovered in the science laboratory" could fill a volume the size of this book. However, the science laboratory experiences provided in the secondary school frequently reaffirm the belief that science is a rhetoric of conclusion. If the essence of science can only be gained in a science laboratory, particular emphasis must be placed on utilizing this strategy in a manner which will afford such discovery.

It is impossible to provide a single description of the laboratory teaching strategy. The two continua outlined in Figure 6-5 loosely portray the types of laboratory experiences provided secondary school students.

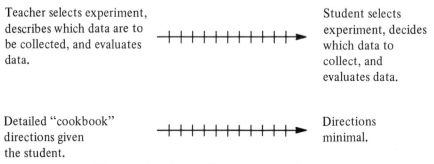

Teacher selects experiment, describes which data are to be collected, and evaluates data.

Student selects experiment, decides which data to collect, and evaluates data.

Detailed "cookbook" directions given the student.

Directions minimal.

Figure 6-5. Types of laboratory experiences.

There may be a time and a place for each type of laboratory activity. There are times when the student should perform experiments which prove points already made and there are times when detailed "cookbook" directions are necessary. However, laboratories of this nature do not project the essence of science, and, in general, *they should be avoided.* When the teacher decides which experiments are to be run and what data to collect and when he evaluates the data, he may be the only person involved in inquiry. The student should be led to the belief that he is experimenting, that he is designing experiments and evaluating conclusions, not simply collecting information in a machinelike manner.

Many of the newer curricular materials were designed to include pre- and postlaboratory discussions. The prelaboratory discussion is used to collect, compare, and contrast data collected, and in many cases it is used to draw conclusions. The success of these new curricula is determined by the extent to which students actually become involved or participate in the activity.

Teachers who assign "cookbook" laboratory experiences assume that students enjoy following directions which prove that the teacher is right. Anyone studying adolescents soon discovers that they enjoy designing and carrying out experiments but that they avoid and often abhor following directions and proving the teacher right. If a teacher wants his charges to enjoy and pursue science, he must make an intense effort to plan laboratory experiences which at least give students the illusion that they are inquirers, that they are designing experiments and evaluating the data they collect.

ADVANTAGES

1. The laboratory strategy tends to provide more concrete experiences than other strategies. This obvious advantage stems from the student's innate desire to manipulate objects and things. The advantage is shallow because the data derived from the manipulations is usually more important than the manipulation.
2. The laboratory strategy affords the student an opportunity to discover the essence of science. This is only true if the student is the designer and evaluator of the laboratory experiments.

DISADVANTAGES

1. The laboratory strategy is more expensive.
2. The laboratory strategy is more time-consuming.

Field Trips

The field trip is an infrequently used strategy which probably ranks second to the lecture strategy in the extent to which it is abused. A field trip should be a well-planned excursion, a trip to a special location which provides students the opportunity to manipulate knowledge they possess. A field trip which does not provide students an opportunity to manipulate knowledge (to apply, analyze, synthesize, and evaluate) may have only entertainment value.

The teacher preparing for a field trip must make many arrangements. Buses must be ordered, parental permission obtained, chaperones solicited, and local conditions arranged. It is imperative that the teacher visit the proposed area at some earlier time. As in any other situation, precise plans must be made and objectives must be constructed. If a resource person other than the teacher will provide some, or part of, the instruction, it should be ascertained that he is acquainted with the objectives. If this resource person does not feel that the teacher's objectives are appropriate, the teacher may find it necessary to seek out another resource person, or to change his objectives. Generally, resource people appreciate knowing the objectives and will help the teacher achieve them as well as those that they may suggest.

The teacher's principal function on a field trip should be to act as perception director. As a perception director the teacher should provide students with questions, worksheets, and study guides which will focus the student's attention on what he knows and what he sees. This does not mean that the student should be directed from cage to cage, or exhibit to exhibit. A few divergent and evaluative questions can effectively channel student activity without restricting movement.

The student participating in a field trip should realize exactly what he is expected to accomplish and how he can reach that goal. He must realize that though the trip is entertaining it is also an educational trip.

ADVANTAGES

1. The field trip may provide the student an opportunity to apply textbook knowledge in an interpretation of a local phenomenon.
2. The field trip may permit students to observe and study something which cannot be brought into the classroom.

DISADVANTAGES

1. Arranging a good field trip consumes a considerable amount of time.
2. Transporting the student to the area being studied may be expensive.

Science Projects and Research Reports

Both science projects and research reports emphasize individual student effort. They involve extended reading in a specific area, some writing, and, in the case of the project, an experiment. Their success is determined by the extent to which the student becomes involved. If the principal motivation stems from a student's desire to get a grade rather than active interest in the subject, the value of the project must be questioned.

A few years ago science projects were required in many schools. Today the emphasis on this dimension of instruction has waned. The principal cause of the decline of the science project as an instructional tool has probably been a lack of local support for these efforts. Though elaborate laboratories and abundant sources of resource personnel facilitate science project work, they are by no means an absolute prerequisite. Resource personnel have typically given freely of their time in these efforts. Schools, however, have not typically provided the equipment, space, and personnel for project work.

The teacher's function should be to direct students along productive paths. He should know the literature of his discipline well enough to direct students toward recent publications and other resource materials. If the project or research paper is a course requirement, the teacher must also guide a student toward an area of research which fits the individual's capabilities and interests.

The student participating in research paper writing or project work should feel that he is actively participating in the effort. That is, he should feel that he can decide which literature to read or experiment to run and what data to collect. Though teacher and parent guidance are necessary and appropriate, the student should feel that the success and/or failure of the venture is his responsibility.

ADVANTAGES

1. Research papers and projects may provide the individual with an opportunity to discipline himself.
2. They may give individuals with special talents an opportunity to prove themselves.
3. They may permit the student to discover a more realistic picture of science. (An extended period of study reflects the nature of science more accurately.)
4. They may provide the gifted student the opportunity to pursue an in-depth study in an area of particular interest to him.

DISADVANTAGES

1. These strategies favor the independent student. The student who, for one reason or another, has not developed independent study skills may suffer.
2. It may be difficult to determine the extent to which the individual has participated.

The six strategies discussed on the previous pages are the major strategies you will use in teaching groups. Each of these strategies may be supplemented by films, filmstrips, or television presentations.

You may have noted that we have avoided examining the terms *discovery teaching*, *inquiry teaching*, and *expository teaching*. These terms refer more to a style of teaching than to a strategy and are perhaps best used to describe what the student does rather than what the teacher does. For example, the lecture method, which is so thoroughly damned by so many, may induce inquiry in spite of the fact that it is expository. And a high inquiry level case analysis can be turned into dogmatic expository teaching.

The good teacher examines the content that is to be taught, reviews and evaluates the available instructional materials, and hypothesizes which materials are best for his particular students. He then proceeds in a hypothetical manner to evaluate the strategy with his students. If, as a result of his efforts, the students are able to demonstrate the defined terminal behaviors, he proceeds. If the student cannot demonstrate the defined terminal behaviors, he reviews his efforts and selects or designs another strategy.

Discussion Questions

1. List ten criteria you could use to help you decide which teaching strategy to use on a given day.
2. Which five criteria of the ten you listed are the most important? Defend your position.
3. Assume that you wanted to develop a longing to know and understand in your students. Which strategies would be the most appropriate for attaining this goal? Explain your reasoning.
4. Examine the other six values expressed by the educational policies commission. How could or should these statements influence your choice of teaching strategies?
5. Is there a "best" strategy?

Additional References

Alyea, Hubert N., and Frederic B. Dutton. *Tested Demonstration in Chemistry.* Eaton, Pa.: Division of Chemical Education, American Chemical Society, 1965.

Barnard, J. Darrell. *Ideas for Teaching Science in the Junior High School.* Washington, D.C.: National Science Teachers Association, 1963.

Barthelemy, Richard E., James R. Dawson, and Addison E. Lee. *Innovation in Equipment and Techniques for the Biology Teaching Laboratory.* Boston: D.C. Heath, 1964.

Joseph, A., P. F. Brandwein, E. Morholt, H. Pollack, and J. F. Castka. *A Source Book for the Physical Science.* New York: Harcourt Brace Jovanovich, Inc., 1961.

Klinkmann, Evelyn (Supervisor). *Biology Teacher's Handbook,* 2nd ed. New York: John Wiley & Sons, Inc., 1970.

Miller, David F., and Glen W. Blaydes. *Methods and Materials for Teaching the Biological Sciences.* New York: McGraw-Hill Book Company, 1962.

Mills, Lester C., and Peter M. Dean. *Problem Solving Methods in Science Teaching.* New York: Teachers College, Columbia University, 1960.

Morholt, Evelyn, Paul F. Brandwein, and Alexander Joseph. *A Sourcebook for the Biological Sciences,* 2nd ed. New York: Harcourt Brace Jovanovich, Inc., 1962.

Porter, T. R. *Biological Science Teaching Tips from TST.* Washington, D.C.: National Science Teachers Association, 1967.

Porter, T. R. (Selector). *Earth-Space Science Teaching Tips from TST.* Washington, D.C.: National Science Teachers Association, 1967.

Porter, T. R. (Selector). *Physical Science Teaching Tips from TST.* Washington, D.C.: National Science Teachers Association, 1967.

Steeves, Frank L. *Readings in the Methods of Education.* New York: Odyssey Press, 1964.

Woodburn, John, and Ellsworth S. Obourn. *Teaching the Pursuit of Science.* New York: The Macmillan Company, 1965.

UNESCO Sourcebook for Science Teaching. New York: UNESCO, 1956.

individualized instruction

Why doesn't John like science? Why does Bill act bored with science class yet rush home to work on a science project in his basement? Why do many girls and some parents express the belief that science is a boy's subject? Is it possible to make science a meaningful subject to more students?

It is assumed that if science instruction were individualized or carefully fitted to the capabilities of each student, these questions would be answered and the problem of making science meaningful to each student would be solved. This chapter summarizes the argument for individualized science instruction, cites patterns of individualization, and describes an individualized science curriculum that has been used successfully in a wide variety of educational settings.

The Individual and Meaningfulness

The teacher facing a class of thirty on the first day has an impossible task. "Who are they?" "What have they done?" "What can they do?" "Will whatever I do be too hard for some and boring to others?" "What can I do that will be meaningful to everyone?"

Ausubel[1] indicates that instruction is meaningful when the individual has the desire and ability to relate the incoming instruction to something he has already learned. Accordingly, learning will occur when the individual has the necessary background and the desire or set to learn. Procedures for determining the student's cognitive background and designing instruction from that point are available, and the only deterrent is time. Developing and maintaining a student's desire or set for school learning is by far the most difficult task.

The Individual and School Learning

Individuals differ in their aptitudes for particular kinds of learning. A number of tests have been designed to measure these aptitude differences and a correlation of $+0.70$ or higher between these aptitude test scores and student achievement is commonly reported.[2] The highly significant correlation between aptitude measures and student achievement has led many teachers to infer that only a few select students can achieve mastery of any given subject. That is, only those students with the highest aptitude level can learn the complex ideas of a given area and most students can only be expected to grasp the least complex ideas of the subject.

Proponents of individualized instruction usually assume that the highly significant correlation between achievement and aptitude is an indication of the effectiveness of present teaching practices which tend to focus instruction on groups rather than individuals. Many researchers and teachers share Carroll's view of aptitude.[3] According to Carroll, aptitude is the amount of time required by the learner to attain mastery of a learning task. If this definition is correct, then subject-matter mastery is theoretically available to each student if we can find the time and means of treating him individually. Today individualized instruction is possible, though it will often take an extensive amount of the teacher's time to solve the many logistical problems involved in getting the right student to the right experience. Many mistakes (placing the wrong student in the wrong experience) will be made. In addition to the logistical problems associated with providing science experiences for each individual, the problem of designing, collecting, purchasing, cataloguing, and

---

[1] David P. Ausubel and Floyd G. Robinson, *School Learning: An Introduction to Educational Psychology* (New York: Holt, 1969).

[2] Benjamin S. Bloom et al., *Formative and Summative Evaluation of Student Learning* (New York: McGraw-Hill, 1970).

[3] John Carroll, "A Model of School Learning," *Teachers College Record*, Vol. 64 (1963), pp. 723–33.

storing these materials frequently appears to be impossible. That, however, is not the point. It is now possible to individualize science instruction for large groups of students. In fact, many schools are already accomplishing this feat.

Patterns of Individualization

An idealized version of individualized instruction involves providing each child with the opportunity to pursue his "own thing" at his own pace with capable tutors available to assist him over, under, around, or through some real or imagined obstacle to his progress. Such a system is financially impossible when education of the entire population is the stated objective. Because providing tutors for each child is financially impossible, it has become essential to design systems of individualized instruction which could be used with large groups of students. Four possible systems have been tried; none have received the attention they deserve.

Length of Instruction

The length of the school year has traditionally been the same for all students in spite of the fact that students learn at different rates and that hundreds of school buildings lie idle all summer while many teachers seek menial employment. Some schools have extensive summer programs, but these are generally designed to provide additional work or repetition. What is necessary is a new kind of educational system which would provide successful learning experiences for those who are disenchanted or perhaps "turned off" by traditional schooling.

In recent years the nongraded elementary school, when properly deployed, has in effect altered the length of instruction for many students. The successes of many nongraded elementary programs suggests that a much broader application of this principle is warranted.

Career Planning

A second alternative is to prepare each student for his prospective adult role. This alternative has received meager support because it is so difficult to predict reliably the student's adult role. Today this is almost impossible because most elementary school students will find employment in jobs which do not now exist.

Early attempts to provide this type of individualization produced the academic, mechanical, and clerical curricular pathways. The mechanical and clerical curriculums have been enhanced by work-study programs which provide an opportunity for immediate application of knowledge. Formal work-study programs have not been established in academic areas, but the value reported by the few students given the opportunity to spend a summer in a scientist's laboratory suggests that we have neglected this type of training.

Differing-Treatments Plan

The rate of learning can be affected by the media employed in teaching. The media may act differentially, permitting some to learn and inhibiting others.[4] Under a differing-treatments plan to individualize instruction, different segments of the population receive different treatments (that is, lecture, laboratory, film, and so on), each of which is designed to accomplish the same objectives. The successes of differing-treatments plans are related to the ability of teachers to match students with an appropriate treatment and the fact that using alternate strategies frequently enhances achievement. Because rules for matching students with appropriate media are not available, the best means of operating a differing-treatments plan may be designing the alternate strategies and encouraging students to make their own selection. Simply providing the students this extra privilege will in many cases cause significant additional achievement.

The Core-Plus Plan

The core-plus plan for individualizing instruction is illustrated by Figure 7-1.

The core materials and experiences are completed by all students. The remedial and review exercises are designed to assist student progress along the core and are only completed by the student when needed. The enrichment exercises are designed to provide challenging "fun-type" experiences which permit the student to use the ideas he has learned in new situations. The Intermediate Science Curriculum Project developed under the direction of Ernest Burkman at Florida State University is essentially a core-plus plan.

Very little effort is needed to convince teachers that individualization of instruction is essential. Many teachers are already involved in individualizing science instruction and have, in effect, individualized portions of their courses for years. Science projects (see Chapter 13) and other extracurricular activities have been used extensively to permit students to pursue science on an in-

---

[4] William Inskeep, *The Effectiveness of a Multiple Media Approach in Teaching Certain Concepts in High School Chemistry*, unpublished doctoral dissertation, Indiana University, 1968.

Enrichment Exercises

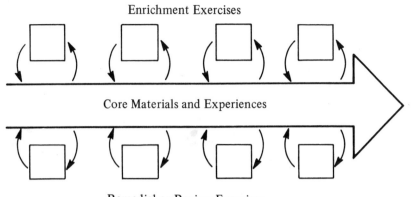

Core Materials and Experiences

Remedial or Review Exercises

Figure 7-1. A core-plus plan.

dividual basis. The "open-ended" laboratory, similarly, is an attempt to encourage the individual student to design *his* experiment, to collect *his* data, to evaluate *his* findings, and to draw *his* conclusions. All these efforts are excellent, but they have not been enough. Too many secondary school students continue to be frustrated by the pace and sequence of science instruction and both these elements of instruction can be modified with relative ease.

Most of this chapter will be used to describe the approach to individualizing science instruction used in the Intermediate Science Curriculum Study (ISCS). The authors of this text and the developers of the ISCS program freely admit that the ISCS is not an ideal program. The prime objective of ISCS writers was to develop a system of individualized instruction that could be implemented *immediately*. To design a system of individualized instruction which could be implemented immediately, the developers had to make many compromises. For example, many excellent experiments had to be left out simply because the cost of supplies and equipment might prohibit their use in the average classroom. The use of a computer was similarly rejected on the grounds that most schools would find it difficult to implement a computer-based system of instruction. However, the computer was used extensively in the field-testing phases of the project.

The ISCS Program

Development

The ISCS materials were developed by teams including such people as scientists, science educators, junior high school teachers, administrators, and specialists in computer-assisted instruction. The basic development sequence adopted by the ISCS project was to develop, field-test, and revise until the material achieved the desired terminal behaviors in students.

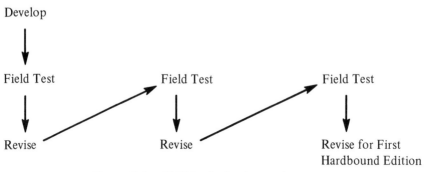

Figure 7-2.   ISCS basic development sequence.

A few activities needed very little revision. Many activities were revised extensively, and many were eliminated. Most of the actual writing was completed on the campus of Florida State University, where the teams of writers from all over the country were assembled to write and then revise their materials.

Revisions of the materials were based on data collected from the field-trial centers where junior high school teachers used the materials with their students. The field-trial teachers were directed to use the material as written and to provide feedback to the writers concerning successes and failures of their students in each activity. The experiments and activities not only had to be good, they had to work successfully with junior high school students.

In spite of the compromises that had to be made, the ISCS project team succeeded in developing a system of individualized instruction which has worked successfully in a wide variety of educational settings. (Rural, suburban, and urban junior high schools were used as field-trial centers.) The program is designed to allow the teacher to vary both the pace and sequence of instruction.

Essentially the program permits the teacher to have the student begin where he is and pursue his studies at his own pace following a sequence suited to his capabilities.

How Does the ISCS Work?

In the paragraphs that follow, an attempt is made to describe and illustrate how a student would proceed in the first level of the ISCS material.

After reading this section, you should get a copy of the ISCS materials and make a more complete study. If possible, you should visit an ISCS class because how the material works with students has been and should be the focus of any study of the ISCS program.

A student beginning the program is asked to read materials. The materials have been designed to communicate to the student what he is to do and what materials he needs for these activities. The "textlike" materials were designed to contain explicit information that could be read by most students. However, it is assumed that the teacher will always be present to assist (and only to assist), but not to tell the student answers or do the student's work. In addition to the "textlike" materials, illustrations are used to clarify the meaning of the words and activity frames (see Figure 7-3) provide both verbal

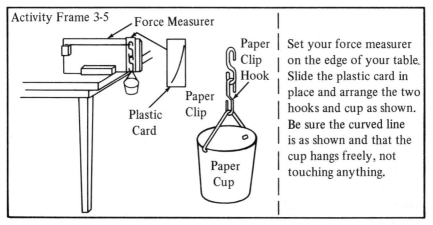

Figure 7-3. Illustration of ISCS printed material and activity frame. (Reprinted from *Preparing the ISCS Teacher*, copyright 1970 by the Florida State University. Reprinted by permission of the publisher.)

and pictorial illustrations of what to do. The printed and pictorial messages are designed to contain the same information, thus permitting even the poorest reader to progress with minimal assistance from the teacher. Figure 7-3 illustrates the planned redundancy of the printed and pictorial messages.

As the students proceed through the printed and pictorial material, the teacher moves among them, answering questions, asking questions, encouraging some students to speed up and others to slow down, and assisting wherever necessary. The student periodically encounters a "checkup frame." (See Figure 7-4.)

Checkup frames are placed at strategic points in the sequence the student is following. This particular checkup frame is located at a point in the sequence where the student is first called upon to carry out mathematical operations with decimals. When the student completes the checkup exercise, he is directed to turn to another page in the book to find the answers. The page the student is directed to is the first page of an additional activity called an excursion. The answers to the checkup-frame questions are given at the beginning of the excursion. (See Figure 7-5.) In this particular case, all students are directed to complete the excursion because working with decimals is an integral part of the course. In the experimental editions of this material, only the students

CHECKUP

Solve the following:

1. $3.7 \times 2.5 =$

2. $0.9 \times 4.6 =$

3. $0.2 \overline{)\ 8.46} =$

To check your answers, see **Excursion 2.**

Figure 7-4.   ISCS Checkup Frame. (Reprinted from *Probing the Natural World I*, p. 14. Copyright 1970 by the Florida State University. Reprinted with permission.)

who could not do the checkup-frame problems were directed to complete the exercise. It was discovered that all students profited from the excursion and it is now essentially a required activity. Most excursions are not required.

There are two types of excursions. Some are designed to develop the student's ability to complete the core materials successfully and others are designed to extend the student's abilities above the core level. The students are referred to an excursion from either a checkup frame or from an activity, as illustrated in Figure 7-6.

The preceding text and illustrations provide examples of the core materials and the excursions. Figure 7-7 provides a general description of the remedial and enrichment excursions that have been designed for the first four chapters of the first level (seventh-grade science).

The ISCS has developed materials for the seventh, eighth, and ninth grades. All of these materials use the basic core-plus design; however, the nature of the materials is changed extensively. Both content and processes are progressively developed in a hierarchical fusion from simple to complex. The increased complexity in content and process is illustrated by the ISCS content flow charts for levels I and II. (See Figures 7-8 and 7-9.)

The content flow charts (Figures 7-8 and 7-9) summarize the arrangement of content and processes within the ISCS program. Examine the logical flow

Operating
with Decimals

Excursion 2

PURPOSE *Remedial*. To provide background in and practice with decimal operations (addition, subtraction, multiplication, division)
APPROXIMATE TIME   60 minutes

When you describe large numbers, you are really using what we call *place values*. A diagram of place values is shown below:

Figure 2-1

0,	0	0 0,	0	0 0.	0	0	0

MILLIONS — HUNDRED THOUSANDS — TEN THOUSANDS — THOUSANDS — HUNDREDS — TENS — ONES — TENTHS — HUNDREDTHS — THOUSANDTHS

A mile is 5,280 feet. This number in terms of place values is shown below:

Figure 2-2

5, 2 8 0

THOUSANDS — HUNDREDS — TENS — ONES

We read the number as *five thousand two hundred eighty*. Notice that each place value is ten times greater than the one on its right. This is an important idea that you will use from here on. Be sure you understand it.

Each digit* in a decimal stands for a different place value. To add decimals, you must line up the decimal points. This keeps the place values lined up so that tenths are added to tenths, hundredths to hundredths, and so on.

---

*Do you know what a digit is? A digit is any single number, like 0, 1, 2, 3, 4, 5, 6, 7, 8, 9. Notice that 0 is a digit but numbers like 10 and 11 are not. These numbers contain two digits.

Answers to Checkup on Page 14

1. 9.25
2. 4.14
3. 42.3

Whether you missed any of these questions or not, you must do this excursion. You must be able to work with decimals if you are to be successful in this course.

EQUIPMENT
None

Keyed in Chapter 2

Figure 7-5.   First page of Excursion 2. (From *Probing the Natural World I*, Copyright 1970 by the Florida State University. Reprinted with permission.)

ACTIVITY 3-8. Gently remove the marked card, and write your name and the word "washers" on it. When you are finished, your card should look like this.

Measure the distance in centimeters from the zero point to each mark that is on the "washers" card. Record these measurements in the table of Figure 3-5 in your Student Record Book.

Plot the data from the table on the grid in Figure 3-6 of your Student Record Book. If you have any trouble in making the graph, turn to **Excursion 5.**

Figure 7-6.   Referred to on Excursion from an activity. (From *Probing the Natural World I*, p. 28. Copyright 1970 by the Florida State University. Reprinted with permission.)

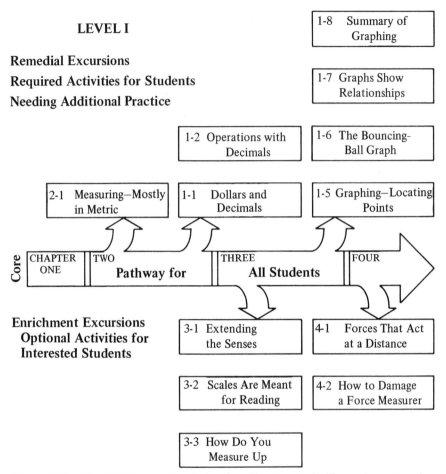

Figure 7-7. The ISCS core-plus design for Chapters 1–4. (From *Preparing the ISCS Teacher*. Copyright 1970 by the Florida State University. Reprinted with permission.)

of content and processes these charts depict and begin thinking about the course(s) you are planning to teach. Designing a flow chart is a logical first step in designing a system of individualized instruction. Once you have designed a flow chart, you can begin specifying performance objectives and selecting strategies to attain these objectives. We do not wish to imply that designing a system of individualized instruction is an easy task. Once the flow charts, objectives, and strategies are designed, you are ready to begin the arduous task of field testing or determining if the materials cause the desired quality and quantity of change in students.

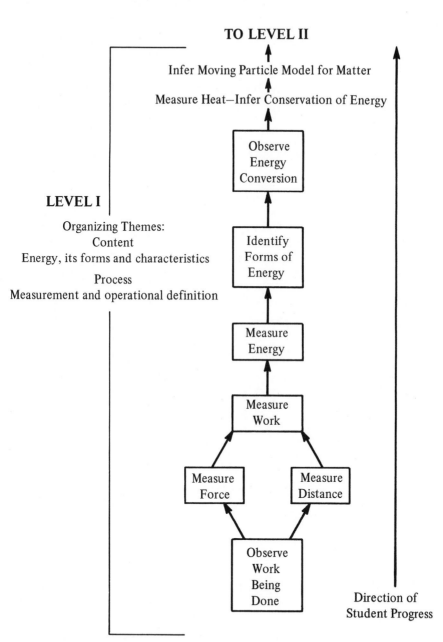

Figure 7-8. Level I content flow. (From *Preparing the ISCS Teacher*. Copyright 1970 by the Florida State University. Reprinted with permission.)

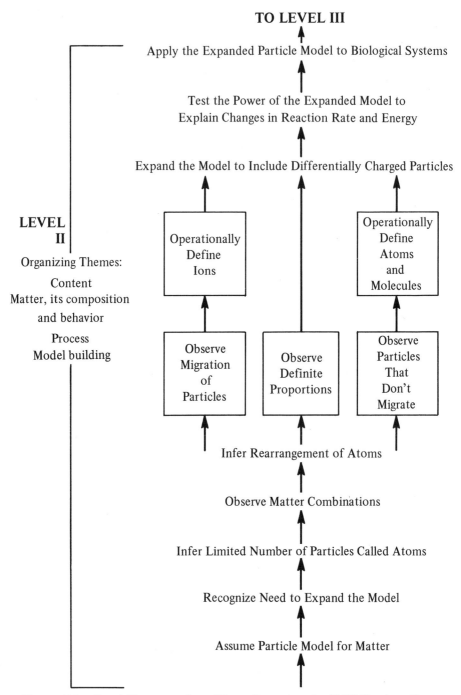

TO LEVEL III

Apply the Expanded Particle Model to Biological Systems

Test the Power of the Expanded Model to
Explain Changes in Reaction Rate and Energy

Expand the Model to Include Differentially Charged Particles

**LEVEL
II**

Organizing Themes:

Content
Matter, its composition
and behavior

Process
Model building

Operationally
Define
Ions

Operationally
Define
Atoms
and
Molecules

Observe
Migration
of
Particles

Observe
Definite
Proportions

Observe
Particles
That
Don't
Migrate

Infer Rearrangement of Atoms

Observe Matter Combinations

Infer Limited Number of Particles Called Atoms

Recognize Need to Expand the Model

Assume Particle Model for Matter

Figure 7-9. Level II content flow. (From *Preparing the ISCS Teacher*. Copyright 1970 by the Florida State University. Reprinted with permission.)

82

Harvard Project Physics

The Harvard Project Physics (HPP) program[5] is similar to the ISCS program in that it utilizes a basic core-plus design. That is, a basic set of experiences that everyone should complete and additional activities that are either elected by students or directed by the teacher. HPP differs from ISCS in that it is designed to accommodate student differences through a multimedia approach. In the ISCS program all students essentially complete the same core of materials; individualization is achieved by altering the pace and sequence of experience. In the HPP program the core of six units can be studied in several different ways. Each unit of the six-unit core contains a wide variety of printed, audiovisual, and laboratory components. For example, a typical HPP unit will contain the following components:

1. A student text and study guide.
2. A laboratory guide which outlines experiments and the apparatus needed to carry them out.
3. A book of physics readings containing everything from reprints of original scientific papers, to historical accounts of great physics achievements, to selections of science fiction. (The *Physics Reader* is designed for browsing and contains materials selected for their ability to arouse the varied interests of different students.)
4. Programed instruction booklets. Some of the programed booklets are designed to provide remedial instruction. Others are used to present core materials.
5. Transparencies for the overhead projector.
6. Silent film loop cartridges.
7. A teacher's guide, which contains a wealth of additional information, including a time schedule and suggested means of using the materials, test items, descriptions of teacher demonstrations, activities students may do at home, and lists of resources other than HPP resources that may be used to supplement the course.
8. Equivalent problem-solving, multiple-choice, and essay unit examinations.

The quantity and diversity of the instructional materials available for each unit exceeds the needs for any one student. The large collection of multimedia materials makes it possible to design a course of study for each child. The designed redundancy of various materials permits an infinite variety of instructional sequences. This flexibility may even be extended to the equivalent

[5] HPP is available through Holt, Rinehart and Winston, New York.

unit examinations where the student could choose to take either the problem-solving, multiple-choice, or essay form of the examination. Because equivalent forms of the examination are available, a student who does not achieve as well as he should on the first examination might elect or be directed to take another form of the examination.

The large amount of material developed for each unit allows the teacher considerable flexibility in designing the unit of experiences for his students. In addition to this within-unit flexibility, the HPP team has designed supplementary units which may be used in conjunction with the six basic units. It is assumed that all HPP classes will complete at least the six basic units but that many classes may complete seven, eight, or even nine units. Fifteen to twenty supplementary units will be available.[6] Some of these units will be designed to fit between units of the basic six-unit core and other units will be designed to follow the basic core. The decision concerning which of the supplementary units to use is left to the teacher.

The Biological Sciences Curriculum Study (BSCS) and the Inquiry Role Approach (IRA)

The Biological Sciences Curriculum Study team not only produced a wide variety of curriculum materials, but stimulated many commercial book companies to do the same. Although the BSCS team did not attempt to design a completely individualized system, it has approached that end through the design of four different introductory texts and a wide range of supplementary materials. An individualized multimedia approach, similar to the HPP approach, could be synthesized from BSCS materials; if other than BSCS materials were also used, the possibilities are essentially unlimited.

The BSCS materials were also field-trial tested in a wide variety of educational settings and revised until the materials were successful with the target populations. The development of the fourth version began when field testing of the first three versions led to the discovery that the materials were too difficult for some students. In the fourth version,[7] illustrations, cartoons, and programed instruction are used extensively to bring students up to the competence level needed to complete the program. The wide range of supplementary materials includes a pamphlet series, laboratory blocks, films, single-topic inquiry film loops, inquiry slides, and a series of paperbacks concerning research problems in biology. An excellent description of all these materials

---

[6] F. James Rutherford, "Flexibility and Variety in Physics," *The Physics Teacher* (May, 1967).

[7] BSCS, *Patterns and Processes* (New York: Holt, 1970).

and directions on how they can be used can be found in the *Biology Teacher's Handbook*[8] and the *Biological Sciences Sourcebook*.[9]

The Inquiry Role Approach (IRA)[10] (also see Chapter 9) to teaching biology was designed to facilitate BSCS instruction. The IRA project team devised a hierarchical sequence of instruction which leads the student from a state of high dependence on the teacher to a state in which the student is the inquirer; the student designs experiments, collects data, and evaluates research findings. In the initial stages of instruction the student is taught specific inquiry roles and learns to work as a member of a team conducting study–search activities. The inquiry functions of the entire team are gradually assumed by each member and he is then encouraged to design and carry out his own inquiry. The organization of students into research teams frees the teacher from his traditional role as the sole information provider. The teacher is thus able to help individuals with problems develop inquiry skills. The end result is a student who can instruct himself, a student who can study independently and achieve. This different approach appears to be a good example of how group processes can be utilized to teach individuals.

The Time Is Now !

It is realistic to predict that within ten years individualized science instruction will be available for all students in all areas of science. Because the teacher's role in a system of individualized instruction differs from the role of the "conventional" teacher and individualized instruction has so many distinct advantages, it is essential to begin preparing to assume this new teaching role.

Some teachers will have the opportunity to begin teaching in schools that have already adopted systems of individualized instruction and these teachers will be able to expend their efforts improving the system. Most teachers, at least those being employed during the first half of the 1970's, will probably be employed to teach in conventional schools where individualized instruction is discussed but not practiced. Teachers in these conventional schools will be faced with the responsibility of adopting systems already developed or of designing their own.

[8] Evelyn Klinckmann, supervisor, *Biology Teacher's Handbook*, 2nd ed. (New York: Wiley, 1970).

[9] Maurice G. Kellogg, Donald L. Troyer, and Hans O. Andersen, *Biological Sciences Sourcebook* (New York: Macmillan, 1972).

[10] Developed by McREL (the Mid-continental Regional Educational Laboratory in Kansas City under the direction of Richard M. Bingman).

It is no longer an impossible task to develop a system of individualized instruction. However, rather than attempting to synthesize an entire system, you should examine the many excellent materials already produced, collect these materials, and assemble them into sequences of instruction. After collecting and sequencing has been completed, you must field-test them with your students. Field-testing with students is essential because all evaluations of the system should be designed to determine the effectiveness of the system with the student. The process of developing a system of individualized instruction is illustrated in Figure 7-10.

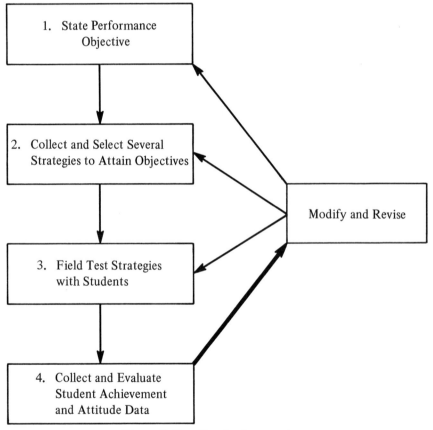

Figure 7-10.   Developing a system.

The developmental testing or field trials can be very expensive, but without testing it is impossible to distinguish reliably between a pretty-looking package of materials which does not work with students and a system which permits each student a maximum amount of success and enjoyment. The fact that developmental testing is so expensive should be considered when planning to individualize science instruction. It will generally be more economical to adopt a system of individualized instruction that is already developed than to attempt to develop one locally. Regardless of which alternative you choose, you must remember that revision and redesign will always be necessary. You must continually collect and evaluate data concerning the program's effectiveness.

Revisions must be made whenever the program fails to develop the desired quality and quantity of change in students.

Discussion Questions

1. When instruction is individualized the teacher usually has a different role to play than when traditional techniques are employed. How might the roles of teachers in individualized teaching situations and traditional situations differ?
2. Describe the single most important characteristic you believe a teacher must develop to be a successful teacher in a system using individualized instruction.
3. List five skills or practices that a teacher of an individualized course will use every day but that a traditional teacher will use only occasionally.
4. Describe what you plan to do about developing the skills and abilities essential to becoming a successful individualizer of instruction.

Additional References

(Note: The three sourcebooks designed to accompany this text contain listings of texts, films, programs, and materials that should help you locate many of the things you will need to individualize instruction.)

Beggs, David W., III, and Edward G. Buffie (eds.). *Independent Study*. Bloomington, Ind.: Indiana University Press, 1965.

Doll, Ronald C. *Individualized Instruction*. Washington, D.C.: American Association for Supervision and Curriculum Development, 1964.

Duncanson, J. P. *Intelligence and the Ability to Learn*. Princeton, N.J.: Educational Testing Service, 1964.

Esbensen, Thorwald. *Working with Individual Instruction: The Duluth Experience*. Palo Alto, Calif.: Fearon Publishers, Inc., 1968.

Gagné, Robert M., ed. *Learning and Individual Differences*. Columbus, Ohio: Charles E. Merrill Books, Inc., 1967.

Gallagher, James J. *Teaching Gifted Students: A Book of Readings*. Boston: Allyn & Bacon, 1966.

Gordon, Alice Kaplan. *Games for Growth*. Chicago: Science Research Associates, 1970.

Hittle, David, Frank Stekel, Shirley Stekel, and Hans Andersen. *Physical Sciences Sourcebook*. New York: The Macmillan Company, 1972.

Inskeep, William K. *The Effectiveness of a Multi-media Approach in Teaching Certain Concepts in High School Chemistry*, unpublished doctoral dissertation, Indiana University, 1968.

ISCS. *Probing the Natural World*, Volume 1. Morristown, N.J.: Silver Burdett Company, 1970.

ISCS. Teacher Preparation Committee. *Preparing the ISCS Teacher*. Tallahassee: Florida State University, 1970.

Kellogg, Maurice G., Donald L. Troyer, and Hans O. Andersen. *Biological Sciences Sourcebook*. New York: The Macmillan Company, 1972.

Klinckmann, Evelyn, Supervisor. *Biology Teachers Handbook*, 2nd ed. New York: John Wiley & Sons, Inc., 1970.

Lee, Addison. "The Experimental Approach in Teaching Biology: An Introduction to the B.S.C.S. Laboratory Program," *The American Biology Teacher* (November, 1962).

Lee, Addison E., David L. Lehman, and Glen E. Peterson (eds.). *Laboratory Blocks in Teaching Biology*. Biological Sciences Curriculum Study Special Publication No. 5, 1967.

Macdonald, James B., and Robert Leeper (eds.). *Theories of Instruction*. Washington, D.C.: American Association for Supervision and Curriculum Development, 1965.

Petrequin, Gaynor. *Individualized Learning Through Modular-Flexible Programing*. New York: McGraw-Hill Book Company, 1968.

Pfeiffer, John. *The New Look at Education: Systems Analysis in Our Schools and Colleges*. New York: Odyssey Press, 1968.

Raubinger, Frederick M., and Harold G. Rowe, *The Individual and Education: Some Contemporary Issues*. New York: The Macmillan Company, 1968.

Redfield, David D., and Stewart P. Darrow. "ISCS: Intermediate Science Curriculum Study," *The Physics Teacher* (April, 1970).

Richard, Paul, and Robert B. Sund. "Individualized Instruction in Biology," *The American Biology Teacher* (April, 1969).

Rutherford, F. James. "Flexibility and Variety in Physics," *The Physics Teacher* (May, 1967).

Utgard, Russell O., George T. Ladd, and Hans O. Andersen. *Earth and Space Sciences Sourcebook*. New York: The Macmillan Company, 1972.

Veatch, J., and G. Hayes. "Individualizing Instruction," *National Education Association Journal*, Vol. 55, No. 38 (1966).

In addition to these references, the reader is referred to the references in Chapter 10.

8

evaluating specific performances

In the preceding three chapters general planning, specific performance objectives, and specific teaching strategies have been emphasized. This chapter will present a brief discussion of techniques that will help you evaluate your ability to perform the tasks described in Chapters 1, 2, and 3. Your ability to plan, write specific performance objectives, and design teaching strategies can be measured by college professors and supervisors; however, their evaluation is not as important as an evaluation which indicates the degree of success your materials and plans have with your students. The important question each teacher must ask is, "Are my students capable of performing the desired terminal performances as a result of my efforts?"

In Chapter 2 the teacher's function was defined as "arranging conditions predicted capable of causing the type and desired degree of change in student performance." Emphasizing the active process of arranging conditions suggests constant evaluation, revision, and re-evaluation. Evaluation must be carefully designed! Evaluation which is not carefully designed may not provide the type of information needed for the revision–re-evaluation processes.

The importance of asking questions throughout a teaching session and certainly at the end of the session should be very evident. If a teacher does not constantly evaluate student progress along his predesigned continuum, the teacher may discover that he is the only individual capable of the prescribed terminal performance. The teacher who has not asked any questions may have to repeat the entire instructional sequence. The teacher who has consistently evaluated student performance as it progressed along the continuum may have to repeat only one or two steps of the instructional sequence.

Figure 8-1 portrays the instructional continuum as a series of steps. The

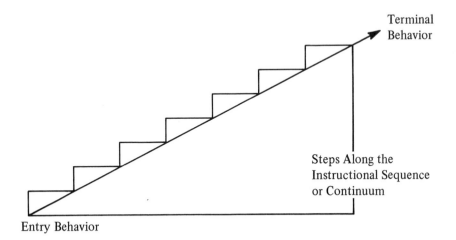

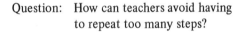

Question: How can teachers avoid having
to repeat too many steps?

Figure 8-1.   Portrayal of an instructional continuum.

inference intended is that each step must be completed before the student can advance to the next step. Though all instruction may not be so arranged, the steps are a fairly accurate portrayal of a typical instructional sequence.

We can then imagine that each step is analogous to a task that the student must be able to perform before he can advance to the next step. If the student did not attain the performance level, he would (figuratively speaking) fall through the structure at that point. Examine this analogy and think back to the suggested lesson plan format. The lesson plan consists of basically three elements: one describing the desired performance, one suggesting a possible strategy, and one evaluating the success of the strategy and/or the appropriateness of the objective.

When instruction is so defined, it is easy to suggest that excellent teaching is the ability to move the entire class up the steps of the continuum or the ability to avoid repetition of any instructional steps. Knowing the precise moment when the student is ready to be led to the next step is the crucial teacher decision. This decision, to be accurate, must be based on data systematically collected by the teacher. Systematic collection of this data is only

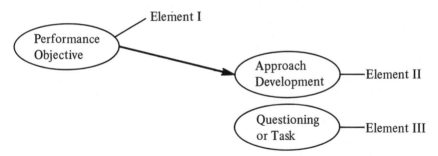

Figure 8-2.   Three elements of a lesson plan.

possible when the teacher designs tasks and questions to measure if the desired terminal performance has been attained.

Questions designed for a given performance objective must be congruent with the objective. If the prescribed terminal performance demands a high level of student thought, the teacher must design a question that will force the thought required by the objective. The contrary is also true. If the teacher wants his students to think, he must design objectives and questions which will demand thought. You may generally assume that students will think at the level you demand. If you do not demand thought, your student's generally will not think! This should caution you to avoid criticizing students for a lack of thought without first examining your instruction to determine the degree or level of thought demanded. The classification systems of Bloom and Guilford may be used in determining the level of thought demanded by your instruction and concomitant questioning. The Guilford model will be advanced as the instrument most appropriate for classifying questions asked by teachers in a classroom discussion setting.[1] The system of Bloom will be used as a model for designing test items.[2] This is strictly author preference. Either system may be used for either purpose.

The Guilford Model

The Guilford system can be used to classify teacher questions as one of five types. These are cognitive-memory questions (CM), convergent-thought questions (CT), divergent-thought questions (DT), evaluative-thought ques-

[1] J. P. Guilford, "The Structure of Intellect," *Psychological Bulletin*, Vol. 53 (1956), pp. 267–93.

[2] Benjamin Bloom, ed. *Taxonomy of Educational Objectives: Handbook I: Cognitive Domain* (New York: David McKay, 1956), 207 pp.

tions (ET), and routine questions. The convergent-, divergent-, and evaluative-thought questions have been termed productive-thought questions for reasons which will become evident as the categories are defined and as examples are given.[3]

Routine questions consist of the conventional management questions asked by teachers. Some examples are

1. Did you put your microscope away?
2. Who has the box of clean slides?
3. Did you work problem No. 23 last night?
4. Did you read Chapter XI?

Cognitive-memory questions demand simple reproduction of facts, formulas, or other items of remembered content through use of such processes as recognition, rote memory, or selective recall. Some examples are

1. When did Einstein publish his theory of relativity?
2. What is the formula for potassium dichromate?
3. How are protozoans classified?
4. Who discovered oxygen?
5. What is biogenesis?
6. How is a hanging drop slide prepared?
7. What were some of the main points of Darwin's theory of evolution?

All of the questions examined can be answered by direct reference to a memory bank. The student does not have to integrate or associate facts. The student's sole responsibility is to select the appropriate response from his bank of stored facts. These comments are not meant to discount the value of teaching facts. Facts are very important. However, if students are not given an opportunity to integrate and associate the facts, the facts will soon be forgotten.[4] The next three categories, referred to as the productive-thought categories, describe the types of questions which force the student to manipulate knowledge. Productive-thought questions enhance the retention and transfer of information by forcing students to integrate and associate the facts.

Convergent thought questions force the student to analyze and integrate stored facts. They are tightly structured questions which lead students toward an expected end result or answer. Some examples of convergent-thought questions are

---

[3] James J. Gallagher and Mary Jane Aschner, "A Preliminary Report on Analysis of Classroom Interaction," *Merrill-Palmer Quarterly*, Vol. 9 (July, 1963).

[4] Ralph W. Tyler, "What High School Pupils Forget," *Education Research Bulletin* (November 19, 1930), pp. 490–92.

1. How does a microscope work?
2. Summarize the sequence of steps you would follow to determine if a given organism was pathogenic.
3. If a car moving at a constant speed travels 4 miles in 4 minutes, what is its speed?
4. What were the major ideas expressed by Darwin in his book *The Voyage of the Beagle*?

Convergent thinking may involve solving a problem, summarizing a body of knowledge, or describing a sequence of techniques, ideas, or premise.

Divergent-thought questions permit the student to generate his own data freely and independently within a data-poor situation or to take a new direction or perspective on a given topic. Some examples of divergent-thought questions are

1. Suppose that a metal object suspended 6 feet above the floor were released. Instead of falling, it moves up. How might the phenomenon be explained?
2. A satellite orbiting the earth may have a large electric charge. You would like to board the satellite. How would you determine whether the satellite was safe to board?
3. If you were selected to be the first man to visit the planet Jupiter, what supplies and equipment would you want to take with you?

Divergent-thought questions reveal the student's ability to begin from an established fact or facts and see further implications or associations that have not been requested. Divergent questions often force self-initiated student performance beyond the teacher's expectations.

Evaluative-thought questions, such as the following, force students to deal with matters of judgment, value, and choice.

1. Who do you believe was the greater scientist, Newton or Einstein? Why?
2. What will the weather be like next week?
3. If you were to use the word *heroic* to describe either Copernicus or Darwin, which scientist would you rate as more heroic?

In the first example the student would have to construct his criteria defining *great scientist* and then decide whether Newton or Einstein was the best example. In the second example the student is asked to make an estimate or give a speculative opinion based on present interpretation of weather conditions. In the third example the student is asked to establish value criteria for the word *heroic* and judge the two individuals on the basis he establishes.

The model described on the previous pages can be very useful in planning because data collected with it can be used to prescribe teacher behavior. The type of questions asked by teachers is very important if transfer of knowledge to new situations is desired. Tyler reported that high school students retained explanations and generalizations significantly better than facts that were not associated or integrated into generalizations and explanations.[5] Explanations and generalizations are formed by the productive-thinking categories described as convergent, divergent, and evaluative in the model. Therefore, the teacher who desires to teach for retention should emphasize productive thinking.

Gallagher and Aschner[6] report that a slight increase in the percentage of divergent questions asked by the teacher produces a large increase in divergent production in children. This indicates that significantly more retention can be caused by the teacher who attempts to ask a few more divergent questions.

This model is, of course, not a panacea. It does not indicate the correct number of each type of question that should be incorporated into each lesson. This is an area worth exploring. Maybe you can discover the best pattern of questioning.

The Bloom Model

The Bloom model was constructed by a Committee of College and University Examiners and published in a book edited by Benjamin Bloom of the University of Chicago.[7] The committee constructed a hierarchical classification system for the goals of our educational system which would permit curriculum developers a means of discussing their goals with much more precision. It is an attempt to classify intended behavior of students which results from their participation in some unit of instruction. This particular handbook deals only with the cognitive domain, that is, with the recall or recognition of knowledge and the development of intellectual abilities and skills.

THE TAXONOMY[8]

1. Knowledge of
    a. Specifics.

[5] Ibid.
[6] Gallagher and Aschner, op. cit., p. 192.
[7] Bloom, op. cit.
[8] Adapted from ibid.

    b. Ways and means.

    c. Universals and abstractions.

2. Comprehension.

    a. Translation.

    b. Interpretation.

    c. Extrapolation.

3. Application.

4. Analysis of

    a. Elements.

    b. Relationships.

    c. Organizational principles.

5. Synthesis of

    a. A unique communication.

    b. A plan.

    c. An abstract relationship.

6. Evaluation.

The model is intended to be a hierarchy of intellectual abilities. It proceeds from the possession of knowledge toward the increased ability to manipulate the knowledge in an intellectual manner. Each step on the hierarchy subsumes the previous step or steps. For example, application involves withdrawing fully comprehended information from the knowledge bank and using it to solve a new problem in a new situation. Application is not possible without comprehension and comprehension is not possible without knowledge, for it is the knowledge that one comprehends.

The model may also be viewed as an internalization gradient. As a student assimilates any bit of knowledge, he may, if provided the opportunity, begin manipulating the knowledge. The manipulations would involve gaining the ability to utilize the knowledge in succeedingly more complex intellectual activities. As the usability of the knowledge advances from comprehension to evaluation, it becomes more and more a part of the individual. Once the individual manipulates the knowledge through the entire range of intellectual activity, he may gain full control of the knowledge, permitting him to use it at any time in any situation. Knowledge so well internalized may never be forgotten.

Once again, it seems appropriate to state that high school students are capable of performing the full range of intellectual activities. However, they will not typically perform at a higher level unless it is demanded. Students prepare for examinations. If examinations demand only recall of knowledge, the student will tend to utilize only those intellectual activities needed to recall information. If examinations consistently demand application, analysis, synthesis, and evaluation, the students will tend to enter the intellectual activities which will prepare them for such an exercise.

In the past, teacher-made tests have failed to demand the higher-level performances. The results reported from a study conducted in West Virginia emphasize this point.

Percentage of Test Items in Each Category*

	Knowledge	Compre-hension	Appli-cation	Analysis	Synthesis	Evaluation	Number of Items
General Science	88.55	8.79	5.65	0.00	0.00	0.00	1,114
Biology	84.71	13.96	0.95	0.30	0.05	0.00	7,954
Chemistry	64.50	20.49	14.86	0.00	0.12	0.00	3,264
Physics	65.06	7.81	27.00	0.06	0.06	0.00	1,715

* Data collected by examining 14,047 test items from final examinations given in 1963.

From a paper presented at the annual meeting of the National Association for Research in Science Teaching, Chicago (February, 1968), by Milton Jacobson of the University of Virginia.

Since 1963 considerable emphasis has been placed on test-item construction. There are probably many more application, analysis, synthesis, and evaluation questions present on tests constructed today.

Examples and definitions of each category of the taxonomy follow:

    I. Knowledge. Knowing something at the knowledge level simply means that the student is able to *recognize* or *recall* the information. The emphasis is on *remembering*. If the student has *remembered*, it is assumed that he will be able to recall the remembered information when the appropriate stimulus is provided.

    A. Knowledge of terminology and specific facts.

        1. The most appropriate definition of a vacuole is

            a. A small spherical membraned enclosure within a cell which contains a fluid.

            b. A small spherical area within a cell which contains a solid or a fluid.

            c. A small, usually spherical membraned enclosure within a cell which contains a solid, a fluid, or both.

      d. A small, usually spherical enclosure within a cell which contains a solid, a liquid, or both and which is surrounded by dense cytoplasm.

    2. Priestly left England because he

      a. Discovered oxygen.

      b. Did not like the king.

      c. Held unpopular religious views.

      d. Owed too many people too much money.

B. Knowledge of processes, conventions, trends and sequences, classifications and categories, criteria, and methodology.

    1. To discover if a given bacterium is motile

      a. Stain it with gentian violet and examine it under the oil immersion lens of a microscope.

      b. Stain it with a vital stain and examine it under the oil immersion lens of a microscope.

      c. Prepare a hanging drop slide of the bacterium and examine it under the high-dry lens of a microscope.

      d. Prepare a hanging drop slide of the bacterium and examine it under the oil immersion lens of a microscope.

    2. The stages of the life cycle of a butterfly are in order:

      a. Pupa, larva, egg, adult.

      b. Larva, egg, pupa, adult.

      c. Egg, pupa, larva, adult.

      d. Pupa, egg, larva, adult.

      e. Egg, larva, pupa, adult.

    3. The study of insects is called

      a. Limnology.

      b. Entomology.

      c. Zoology.

      d. Insectology.

      e. Helminthology.

    4. The criteria used to separate the phylum Protozoa into its classes is

      a. Type of locomotion.

      b. Presence and size of the flagella.

      c. The type of food they "eat."

      d. The size of each group.

C. Knowledge of principles, generalizations, and theories.

    1. Which one of the following equations is the best representation of the process of photosynthesis:

a. $CO_2 + H_2O \xrightarrow[\text{chlorophyll}]{\text{light}}$ Carbohydrate $+ O_2$.

b. $6CO_2 + 6H_2O \xrightarrow[\text{chlorophyll}]{\text{light}} C_6H_2O_6 + 6O_2$.

c. $6CO_2 + 12H_2O \xrightarrow[\text{chlorophyll}]{\text{light}} C_6H_{12}O_6 + 6H_2O + 6O_2$.

d. $6CO + 6H_2O \xrightarrow[\text{chlorophyll}]{\text{light}} C_6H_{12}O_6 + 6H_2O + 6O_2$.

e. $6CO + 12H_2O \xrightarrow[\text{chlorophyll}]{\text{light}} C_6H_{12}O_6 + 6H_2O + 6O_2$.

2. The *mass action expression* indicates that
   a. For every action there is an equal and opposite reaction.
   b. Every chemical reaction has its own specific equilibrium state in which there is a definite relationship between the concentration of materials.
   c. Every chemical reaction attempts to form an equilibrium between reactants, but is never able to do so.
   d. Whenever a reaction reaches equilibrium, nothing that you might do to the reaction will upset the equilibrium.

II. Comprehension. The student demonstrating comprehension indicates that he has an understanding of the literal message contained in a communication. Comprehension is demonstrated when the student is able (1) to put the communication into other language or other terms; (2) to place a communication into another form, like a chart or a graph or interpret information given in graphic form; or (3) to make estimates or predictions based on an understanding of the trends, tendencies, or conditions described in the communication.

A. Translation is the ability to paraphrase or describe in other terms.
   1. Haeckel's statement of the recapitulation theory was, "Ontogeny recapitulates phylogeny." In your own words explain Haeckel's statement of this theory.
   2. A straight stick placed upright in a tank of water appears to be bent at the surface. This is due to
      a. Dispersion.
      b. Interference.
      c. Polarization.
      d. Reflection.
      e. Refraction.

B. Interpretation is the ability to manipulate a translation. The ability to recognize or make inferences from material presented in a variety of forms including paragraphs, tables, charts, graphs, or even cartoons.

1. Examine the graph.

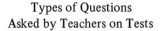

Types of Questions
Asked by Teachers on Tests

Make your judgment *only* in terms of the information given. Mark the question

(a) If the item is true.

(b) If not enough information is given.

(c) If the item is false.

_____ (1) Chemistry teachers make students think more than biology teachers do.

_____ (2) Teachers ask more knowledge questions than all other kinds added together.

_____ (3) Teachers rarely ask analysis, synthesis, or evaluation type questions.

_____ (4) Chemistry teachers ask more application questions than both biology and general science teachers.

_____ (5) Simple recall of knowledge receives the greatest emphasis in general science.

C. Extrapolation involves the ability to go beyond the limits of the data or information given and make correct applications and extensions of the data or information. These extensions will generally fall within the following areas:

1. An extension of the time dimension involving an attempt to extend the trends and tendencies to other time periods.
2. An extension from one topic or domain to another relevant topic or domain.
3. An extension from a sample to a universe or from a universe to a sample.

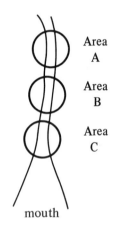

mouth

a. A species has been defined as any population of animals or plants which will interbreed. A zoologist studying clams in a long river discovered that clams in Area A could interbreed with clams in Area B and that clams in Area B could interbreed with clams in Area C, but that clams in Area A could not interbreed with clams in Area C. Mark the question:
(a) If it is definitely true.
(b) If it is possibly true.
(c) If not enough information is given.
(d) If it is probably false.
(e) If it is definitely false.

_____ (1) According to the definition, the clams in A, B, and C are not the same species.

_____ (2) The clams in A, B, and C may have been the same species earlier in their history.

_____ (3) According to the information given, the clams in A, B, and C are becoming the same species.

_____ (4) Separate species of clams may be forming in each area because they are geographically isolated.

b. You have noted that an apple falling near the surface of the earth is accelerated toward the earth at a rate of 32 feet per second. [Acceleration $= G(M/D^2)$.] You also know that acceleration is inversely proportional to the square of the distance from the earth's center. And the moon is about sixty times further away from the center of the earth than is the apple. Determine the rate of the moon's acceleration toward the earth.

c. You have studied the relationship between local climatic conditions and the presence of a large body of water. If Lake Michigan were to disappear, Milwaukee would probably experience winters which were

(1) Warmer and drier.

(2) Colder and drier.

(3) No different than present.

(4) Drier but about the same temperature.

(5) More humid but about the same temperature.

d. Fossils are formed in sedimentary rock. Marine fossils are found in bedrock thousands of feet above sea level. Which explanation best describes the occurrence of these fossils?

(1) These fossils were probably brought there by glaciers.

(3) The seas must be thousands of feet deeper now than they were at one time.

(3) Marine organisms must have been able to live on land at one time.

(4) The sediments from which these rocks were formed must have been deposited in shallow seas and at a later time the rocks were uplifted.

e. You have just studied the relationship between the earth's inclination and the seasons. Which change would occur if the earth's axis were inclined at an angle of 30 degrees instead of its present 23.5 degrees?

    (1) The equator would receive fewer hours of daylight on June 21.

    (2) The direct rays of the sun would move over a greater area of the earth's surface.

    (3) The latitude of the North Star would be increased by 6.5 degrees.

    (4) The celestial equator would be farther from the zenith.

III. Application. Application questions measure the student's ability to solve new problems in new situations. Applications of knowledge and comprehensions must be made without external direction. The individual must recognize for himself the principles involved and select the correct means for solution. The individual, when facing the new problem, must reach back in his own memory and decide which concepts and principles he can use to solve the problem.

Items which measure application are frequently difficult to differentiate from those that measure comprehension. The diagram illustrates the difference between these two levels. An item which measures application forces the student to go through all six steps. A comprehension item provides the student all the information of steps 1–4 and the student only completes steps 5–6.

1. Determine the rate of the moon's acceleration toward the earth. (Compare this example to the second comprehension example. Notice the information provided in that example is much more complete.)

2. A man fishing in a small lake snags a large piece of iron which he lifts into his boat. The level of the water in the lake will
   a. Rise.
   b. Drop.
   c. Remain unchanged.

3. Complete the following reactions:
   $NH_4Cl + NaCH \rightleftharpoons$
   $NH_4Cl + KOH \rightleftharpoons$

4. You are about to begin collecting maple syrup from a tree for the first time in your life. How deep into the tree should you cut?

5. Dick inflated his basketball from a large 100-psi air tank. Bill inflated his at the same time using a small hand pump. They immediately checked and found that when dropped from the same height, A, each ball would rebound to precisely the same

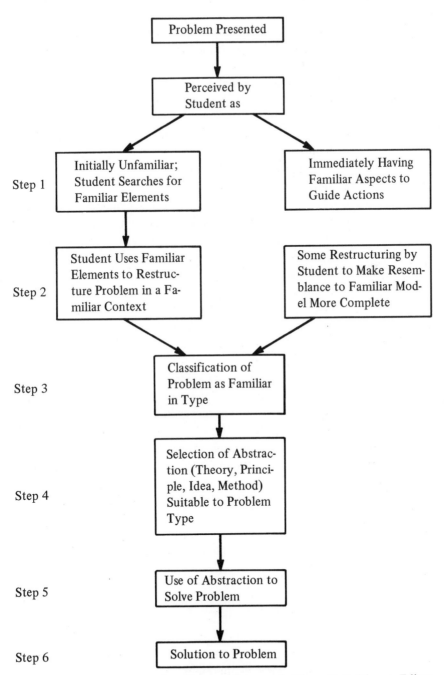

Figure 8-3. The process of application diagramed. (From B. S. Bloom, Editor, *Taxonomy of Educational Objectives: Hand Book I: Cognitive Domain.* New York: David McKay, 1956. Reprinted with permission of the publisher.)

height, *B*. An hour later they again dropped the balls from height *A* to the same surface as before. Assuming no leakage, you would expect that

   a. Both rebounded higher than *B*.

   b. Dick's rebounded higher than *B*, but Bill's rebounded lower than *B*.

   c. Dick's rebounded lower than *B*, but Bill's rebounded higher than *B*.

   d. Both rebounded higher than *B*.

   e. Both rebounded lower than *B*.

6. Core drilling in a geosynclinal reveals sedimentary rock layers that are as much as 40,000 feet thick. Which is the most reasonable explanation for the presence of such thicknesses?

   a. Sediments were deposited in basins that were originally 40,000 feet thick.

   b. Sedimentary rocks have been uplifted by orogenic processes.

   c. Sediments accumulated in basins that were sinking and being filled at the same time.

   d. Sedimentary rocks were formed at the same time the earth's crust was formed.

7. Consider the situation: The length of 1 degree of latitude on planet A is 50 miles. On planet B, 1 degree of latitude is 100 miles in length. If a sailor was standing on the deck of a ship on a large ocean on each planet and looked at the horizon, how would the distance between the sailor and the horizon compare on the two planets?

   a. Greater on planet A than on planet B.

   b. Greater on planet B than on planet A.

   c. The distance would appear to be the same on both planets.

   d. Given data are insufficient to make a comparison.

IV. Analysis. Analysis items test a student's ability to break a problem or idea into its component parts, indicating that he understands their relationships. They frequently involve

A. Distinguishing facts from hypothesis in a communication.

B. Distinguishing relevant from extraneous material.

C. Uncovering unstated assumptions.

D. Identifying conclusions and supporting statements.

   1. There are two species of pneumococcus bacteria. Type I has

a carbohydrate coat and Type II does not have a coat. Mice injected with Type I all died with pneumonia. Type II had no apparent effect on the mice. Which conclusion(s) may be valid?

  a. The coat contains something which causes pneumonia in mice.

  b. Type I bacteria cause pneumonia in mice.

  c. The coat protects the Type I bacteria.

  d. Type II bacteria are harmless.

  e. Two of the above.

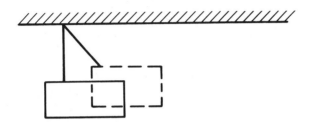

2. A ballistic pendulum may be used to measure the velocity of a bullet. A block of wood is suspended from a string and a bullet is fired into it. If the mass of the block, the mass of the bullet, and the amount of deflection are known, the velocity of the bullet at impact with the block can be computed. Which of the following is assumed in making this computation?

  a. The mass of the bullet is negligible.

  b. No heat energy is dissipated in the block.

  c. The mass of the string is negligible.

  d. Air resistance is negligible.

  e. Two of the above.

3. Which of the following statements most strongly supports the role of the thymus in immunity?

  a. The thymus has many leucocytes.

  b. The thymus has an extensive blood supply.

  c. The thymus is located very close to a portal of disease organism entry.

  d. The thymus is derived from the walls of the embryonic gill pouches.

  e. The thymus is very close to the heart.

V. Synthesis. Synthesis items measure the student's ability to put

elements together to form a new pattern. The emphasis is on original-
ity and creativity which is noticeable when a student

A. Produces a unique communication such as a story or a play.
B. Proposes a plan or set of operations.
C. Analyzes a phenomenon and formulates a hypothesis to explain
   the factors involved.
   1. Describe how the concepts and principles of chemistry may
      be important to you. Your answer must demonstrate a knowl-
      edge of chemistry.
   2. Suppose someone gave you a drug that he said would cure
      cancer. Design a plan to test the product which would permit
      you to get the drug on the market as soon as possible.
   3. How would you discover whether a given organism caused a
      specified disease? (Note: If the student had studied Koch's
      postulates, this item would only measure his knowledge of a
      procedure.)
   4. An irregularly shaped object which appears to be denser than
      air is released from a position above the floor. Instead of
      falling, it rises to the ceiling. Analyze the situation and con-
      struct some testable hypotheses.

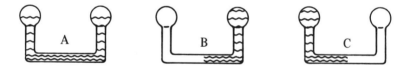

   5. A closed glass container appears as in Diagram A when sus-
      pended in that position. When a person holds one of the glass
      bulbs, the fluid inside flows into the other bulb as in B and C.
      Analyze the situation and construct several testable hypoth-
      eses.
   6. Prepare a list describing all the supplies and equipment you
      would take with you on a two-month trip to Jupiter which
      includes a one-week stay on the planet.

VI. Evaluation. Evaluation questions involve the student in making
    judgments of ideas, works, solutions, methods, or materials. They
    involve the student in using criteria which are provided or which he
    synthesizes.
    A. Discuss the significance of Darwin's theory of evolution. Defend
       your discussion.

B. Criticize the statements of the Neptunian and early Plutonist theorists concerning the origin of the earth. What are the weakest and strongest points of each argument? State your criteria for judging their arguments.

C. Construct a list of characteristics that you would look for when purchasing a car. Examine the information provided on four automobiles. Select the automobile which best fits your criteria.

D. Who do you think was the greater scientist, Newton or Einstein? State your criteria and defend them.

E. What will the weather be like next week? State the criteria you are using to make this judgment.

The six categories of the Bloom model can be very useful in test-item construction and also in attempting to measure the type of thinking you are demanding of students. However, once again the authors must admit that they do not have a prescriptive formula for deriving the correct number of each kind of question. The fact that most students will not have been forced to think at the higher levels in previous school experiences suggests that it might be advisable to begin with a small percentage of higher-level questions and progressively increase the number during the year. The authors suggest the following percentages:

Per Cent of Questions at the Beginning of the Year			Per Cent of Questions at the End of the Year
50	50	Knowledge	10
25	30	Comprehension	30
10	13	Application	35
5	5	Analysis	15
1	1	Synthesis	5
1	1	Evaluation	5

If your students have been given the opportunity to think in their previous school experiences, you may begin with a greater number of higher-level questions. If you have classes of slow learners, you may have to emphasize a greater number of low-level questions. Never assume that slow learners cannot apply, analyze, synthesize, or evaluate. They may need more time to perform these tasks, but they are capable of higher-level thinking.[9]

[9] Harold G. Liebherr and Glen E. Peterson (eds.). *The Teacher and B.S.C.S. Special Materials*, Biological Sciences Curriculum Study, Special Publication No. 4 (1966), 70 pp. Copyright 1966 by the American Institute of Biological Sciences.

The Affective Domain[10]

Of the three domains (cognitive, psychomotor, affective), the affective domain is undoubtedly the most important and most difficult to define. Biologically speaking, this is the energy-release domain. It begins at a point where an individual releases enough energy to receive stimuli, extends through a point where he actively pursues information, to a point where the information becomes such an integral part of the individual that it characterizes him. Each step requires greater involvement from the individual and demands from him a greater expenditure of energy. This is the domain of interests, attitudes, appreciations, values, and biases. This is the domain that is frequently ignored because measurement seems less plausible, and often impossible.

The major significance of this domain lies in its relationship to the cognitive domain. As one proceeds up the cognitive domain from the recall and recognition of knowledge level to the level where judgment or evaluation occurs, an increased amount of energy is necessary. If attitudes are not changed, the concomitant energy release will not equal the quantity necessary for application, analysis, synthesis, or evaluation. Higher-level thought is thus not possible without a concurrent change in student attitude toward the subject. Some students will have the necessary positive attitudes; however, the majority of students will not have a positive attitude, and these students will need to be motivated.

The discussion of this domain is intended to focus teacher attention toward the importance of making those things which should be taught interesting to the students. An attempt to force students to learn material that is not interesting, meaningful, or valuable *to them* is typically a wasted effort.

Gaining student interest is not difficult if you make an effort (1) to begin where they are (the known) and then proceed toward the unknown and (2) to be enthusiastic. It is particularly important that you project enthusiasm for the subject, for the student, and for the school. This point was clearly made by Dean Hanne Hicks, who frequently said, "As much can be caught as taught."[11]

Though more difficult to measure and perhaps more difficult to change, the student's attitude toward science must be measured and if measurement does not reveal a significant positive change, attempts must be made to rectify the situation. The science teacher who fails to cause significant positive atti-

[10] David R. Krathwohl, Benjamin Bloom, and Bertram B. Masia, *Taxonomy of Educational Objectives, The Classification of Educational Goals Handbook II: Affective Domain* (New York: David McKay, 1956), 196 pp.

[11] A frequent statement made by the former Dean of Curriculum and Instruction at Indiana University, Hanne Hicks.

tude change has contributed less to a student's general education than one who fails to teach his students a few facts.

The action verbs suggested in Chapter 5 for use in constructing performance objectives can be useful guides to determining if the student's attitude toward science is changing. Students may demonstrate their attitude toward science in many observable ways. Some ways include

1. *Joining* the Science Club.
2. *Participating actively* in the Science Club.
3. *Reading*
   a. Science journals.
   b. Science fiction.
   c. The science and medicine sections of *Time*, *Newsweek*, and other popular journals.
   d. Science stories in newspapers.
4. *Gathering* collections of specimens.
5. *Visiting* museums and zoos.
6. *Designing* science experiments.
7. *Examining* your bulletin-board displays.
8. *Consulting* outside resources.
9. *Spending* free time after school in your laboratory.
10. *Repeating* science experiments.
11. *Revising* an experiment.
12. *Questioning* all things.

You may not feel that the information collected from observation of a student's affective behaviors can be used to help derive a student's grade, but this does not deride the significance of these behaviors. These student behaviors can and should be used to evaluate your effectiveness as a teacher. You must also remember that Hicks' statement is probably correct. If as much can be caught as taught, emphasizing affective behavior may position the student so that he can catch more.

The Psychomotor Domain

The psychomotor domain encompasses the motor activities that are important in developing the student's ability to manipulate objects and, in general, develop motor skills. According to Bloom, psychomotor ability is rarely measured in the secondary schools or colleges.[12] Bloom's group did

[12] Bloom, op. cit., pp. 7–8.

not believe the development of a classification scheme for this area would be very useful at this time. A review of the literature reveals that very little has been done since publication of the taxonomy, indicating that this area could be an area of productive new research. Research into the role of the psycho-motor domain becomes *particularly eminent* when consideration is given the role of the science laboratory.

The development of psychomotor skills did not become an adjunct to science instruction until around 1960. Prior to that time the teacher-per-formed demonstration was the principal mode of instruction. The teacher was the only individual who needed to perform psychomotor skills with any precision. The new curricula, which all emphasize extensive student partici-pation in laboratory experience, focus considerable emphasis on student per-formance of a wide variety of psychomotor skills. A concomitant emphasis on the evaluation of the student's psychomotor skills is not evident. Evalua-tion is needed to ascertain the student's capacity for manipulating the pre-scribed material and to determine the general effectiveness of the laboratory experience as an instructional strategy.

Research indicating that laboratory experiences are better than many other strategies is encouraging, especially when we remember that the student's laboratory performance is rarely an important factor in determining the grade he will receive in the course. Perhaps this is a reason for its success as a teaching strategy. The authors question the assumption that this lack of emphasis on grading encourages achievement. If a student does an excellent job in the laboratory, this fact should be reflected in his grade. That students are or can be motivated by grades is a factual statement. Furthermore, grades will be a principal motivator until a different means of reward is invented and utilized by teachers.

Excellent laboratory work is not necessarily reflected in a well-written laboratory report, although developing a student's ability to write good reports is an important objective. Excellent laboratory work may be defined as the ability to perform manipulations accurately enough to obtain *repro-ducible results* within the limits of measurement error attributable to the in-struments used. The choice of the words *reproducible results* is intended to emphasize the idea that reproducible results are the products sought through the processes of science.

This nuts-and-bolts definition describes areas of laboratory performance involving psychomotor skills which can be observed and measured with a fair degree of accuracy. In the discussion of psychomotor skills the cognitive and affective functions involved in the successful completion of a manipula-tion have been ignored. It is obvious that all three domains are interacting to cause the phenomenon described as an excellent laboratory performance. An individual must have a knowledge of ways and means of proceeding, an attitude permitting participation, and the requisite psychomotor skills to complete a laboratory exercise successfully. The fact that demonstration of a psychomotor skill in a science laboratory reflects all these interactions strongly supports the argument urging increased emphasis on the psychomotor skills. Some examples of psychomotor skills which can be observed and measured include

1. Making a hanging drop slide in a given amount of time.
2. Transferring bacteria without permitting contamination by foreign organisms.
3. Determining the end point in a titration to within the error allowable.
4. Determining the volume of a solid liquid to within ± 0.1 of a unit.
5. Setting up the apparatus for an experiment in a prescribed manner.
6. Properly using a given piece of apparatus.

Discussion Questions

1. Describe means you might use to discover how your students define the word *science* without formally asking them a question.
2. You have just begun teaching students who have rarely been asked to work above the knowledge and comprehension levels of the taxonomy. You want them to work at the higher levels but your attempts at getting them to apply, analyze, synthesize, and evaluate on your examination have been a dismal failure. What will you do?
3. It's the first week of school. One of your students drops by your room after school. In the course of your conversation with him he says that he never studied science because science was nothing but a worthless collection of facts. What should you do?
4. Assume that a student's perception of science will be strongly influenced by the type of test questions you ask. Describe a test that you believe would be consistent with your definition of science.

Additional References

CUEBS Panel on Evaluation. *Testing and Evaluation in the Biological Sciences.* Washington, D.C.: Commission on Undergraduate Education in the Biological Sciences, 1967.

Dressel, Paul, and Clarence R. Nelson. *Questions and Programs in Science.* Educational Testing Service, 1956.

Gronlund, Norman E. *Constructing Achievement Tests.* Englewood Cliffs, N.J.: Prentice-Hall, Inc., 1968.

Harris, C. W. (ed.). *Problems in Measuring Change.* Madison: University of Wisconsin Press, 1963.

Hedges, William D. *Testing and Evaluation for the Sciences.* Belmont, Calif.: Wadsworth Publishing Co., Inc., 1966.

Lee, Addison. *Testing and Evaluating Student Success with Laboratory Blocks.* Boston: D. C. Heath, 1969.

Nedelsky, Leo. *Science Teaching and Testing.* New York: Harcourt Brace Jovanovich, Inc., 1965.

Nelson, Clarence. *Improving Objective Tests in Science.* Washington, D.C.: National Science Teachers Association, 1967.

Sanders, Norris M. *Classroom Questions: What Kinds?* New York: Harper & Row, 1966.

Schoer, Lowell A. *Test Construction: A Programmed Guide.* Boston: Allyn & Bacon, Inc., 1970.

wanted: an instructional theory for science teaching

The behavioral and natural sciences continue to accumulate descriptions of phenomena. Eventually the descriptions are refined and experimental data are collected to answer questions about origins, causes, and relationships of the phenomena to other observations. As this process continues, a network of explanation evolves. Soon previously isolated phenomena, their descriptions, and their probable causes are linked together by a more general explanation that accounts for all of them. At one stage of development this "network explanation," or theory, is a descriptive tool. As such, given a situation that is within the limits of description of the combined previously investigated phenomena, an operator can reliably categorize it and/or state its cause. At another stage of development, a theory allows the operator to set up the necessary antecedents and bring about a desired effect. This is application. In order to apply, it is necessary to be able to predict outcomes. We think, "If I do *this*, then *that* will occur." Theories this well developed are practical tools.

Imagine science teaching as a technology based on the use of such reliable tools with which to engineer optimal learning in students! It isn't, and we can't, not yet at any rate. The purpose of this chapter is to suggest paths toward the building of such a technology. The literature contains a number of "theories" of learning and human development, some of which are close to being tools of prediction or description. A few of these are worthy of repetition in our orientation. As we focus on the task of building a theoretical structure for science education, we may not lose sight of *why* students are in science (or any) classrooms in American schools. It has been suggested by the Educational Policies Commission that the central purpose of schools must be to develop in children the ability to think.[1] Whatever technological structure we aim at may be relevant only inasmuch as it contributes to the development of this ability.

The work of Bruner, Gagné, Hawkins, and Suchman in the area of learning and instructional theory is relevant to our task, as are the definitional and instructional studies of self-directed inquiry by a regional educational laboratory. Any review presented here is of the briefest sort. For a complete treatment the reader is directed to the authors' original works cited in the footnotes to this chapter.

Jerome Bruner's writings on learning and instruction have been highly influential in education. His work on discovery and the personal nature of coming to know things has been a point of reference for science education research and teaching during the 1960's. Discovery to Bruner is any acquisition of knowledge by the individual through the use of his own mind. He insists that discovery is not a phenomenon exclusive of the frontier or cutting edge of research[2] but may take place whenever a professional, layman, or child rearranges data so as to be able to go beyond it, thus gaining new insight. It is the rearrangement that seems to be crucial, not gathering additional or "key" data. Thus, "discoveries" exist often not as uncovered novelties but as the result of mental manipulation of what is already known. It is just this feature of discovery that, by removing it from the realm of mysterious creation by an elite, has enabled curriculum builders and teachers to consider its use in the classroom. New elementary and secondary science curricula were developed to allow the learner to "come to know" personally through manipulation of things and often quite independently of the teacher. Bruner holds that four benefits accrue to the learner from discovery learning. Included are intellectual potency increase, a change from extrinsic to intrinsic (the satisfaction of discovery itself) rewards, an opportunity to learn the actual mechanics (heuristics) of discovery, and more effective use of memory (efficient methods of storage and retrieval of information).[3]

---

[1] Educational Policies Commission, "The Central Purpose of American Education" (Washington, D.C.: National Education Association, 1961), pp. 5, 12, cited in John W. Renner and William B. Ragan, *Teaching Science in the Elementary School* (New York: Harper & Row, 1968), pp. 50–51 (359 pp.).

[2] Jerome S. Bruner, "The Act of Discovery," *Harvard Educational Review*, Vol. 31 (Winter, 1961), cited in James Raths et al., *Studying Teaching* (Englewood Cliffs, N.J.: Prentice-Hall, 1967), p. 208 (490 pp.).

[3] Ibid., p. 209.

Bruner, as mentioned in Chapter 6, has also moved toward a theory of instruction.[4] He has set up a series of guidelines intended for the use of those who would theorize to facilitate learning. Such theories should be both prescriptive and normative. For the former, they should tell how best to accomplish the desired pupil learnings while enabling evaluation of specific learning or teaching strategies. In the latter case, a theory must present criteria and the conditions under which they may be met. Such criteria must be so broad as to be applicable to a subject-matter discipline rather than merely a certain grade-level within it.

Moreover, a theory within Bruner's limits would tell how to generate within a student a predisposition toward learning. A theory of instruction should tell how to structure the knowledge needed to be learned for optimum understanding. Sequence of presentation of material should be specified. A theory must tell the kinds and frequency of reinforcement during the instruction-learning process. (Recall Kessen or Bruner, Chapter 6, p. 58.)

As will become apparent, many writers on the topic of instructional theory are deeply concerned with structure and sequence. The notions of motivation and reinforcement should not be new to the science education student and should offer a more or less common base of appreciation and understanding in the Brunerian system. However, replacing *what* to teach with *how* to present it so it can be understood presupposes two assumptions. First, the teacher knows what it is that is important for students to know. Second, for students to know they must be able to understand. Accepting that *you* hold these assumptions, you must prepare to defend what you teach and present it with a pattern and order that facilitates understanding it. Without facetiousness this is really all you must do once you have motivated students and a system of intrinsic rewards.

Robert M. Gagné is a cognitive psychologist who has been concerned with the structure of learning.[5] Gagnéian structure has in it the elements of both pattern and sequence. Usually associated with the principle that learning is possible in any of eight types or levels of complexity, for which he sets specific conditions (and holds the assumption that mastery of one type depends upon mastery of those beneath it), Gagné should, for our purposes, be studied primarily for his insistence that knowledge itself is organized into hierarchies of principles which may have to be learned all within one or two of his eight types of learning.[6]

[4] Jerome S. Bruner, *Toward a Theory of Instruction* (Cambridge, Mass.:The Belknap Press of Harvard University Press, 1966), pp. 40–42.

[5] Robert M. Gagné, *The Conditions of Learning* (New York: Holt, 1965), 308 pp.

[6] See ibid., for a complete treatment of the eight types of learning.

Principle learning and problem solving are Gagné's two highest (most subsumptive) levels of learning. He interprets research to indicate that principles can be learned both through expository direct principle-learning procedures and through problem solving. However, the latter has been observed by him to produce high-level understanding and reliably greater retention over time.[7] But lest we view Gagné as an advocate of teaching students *how* to discover, he is quite specific in his rejection of a heuristics or discovery-mechanics orientation for teaching. Subject-matter knowledge, the principles of which are hierarchically arranged, is what the learner must acquire. Knowledge of methods of problem solving by itself would constitute a small part of what a student would require to become a superior problem solver. To be a superior problem solver one would, evidently, have to understand both the content principles of a discipline and their functional relationships. With this background a superior problem solver is seen as one who solves a problem as a result of having combined the applications of principles from seemingly unrelated knowledge hierarchies. This is a behavior that is a cut above generalizing a principle to its intended class of problem situations, and it is a major difference between the routine solver of problems or technician and the creative individual. But the difference, according to Gagné, is mainly due to the superior operators' having subsumed great masses of content understanding arranged in a structural relationship. His content understanding is so extensive and keen that relationships which seem mysterious to the less learned are the stuff of the superior operator's intellectual play. Although it is fascinating to muse on the thought processes such an operator may use, knowledge of such content-free mechanics is not nearly enough to bring the technician up to the superior operator's level.

Gagné entreats us not to be fooled by the motivation generated in children by solving problems or discovering for themselves. Such experiences may generate a drive to learn more and facilitate application and retention of that learned, but it is nonsense to expect that a neophyte learner without benefit of knowledge of vast amounts of related content principles can become a creative thinker.[8]

Thus, before we are caught up with Bruner's suggestion that children can learn how to discover, we may need to deal with Gagné's concern for understanding of structured content. It would be simple to play semantics and say that amassing hierarchies of knowledge and preparing to suggest hypothetical relationships between widely separated hierarchies constitute a me-

[7] Gagné, op. cit., pp. 164–65.
[8] Ibid., p. 168.

chanical tool and hence a "way" to discover. But the division between the camp of heuristics and that of hierarchical connectionism is a real one and not so easy for the educator to dismiss. At its worst it is reflected by the extremes of the no-substance Professor Process Purist and Dr. Rigorous B. Subjectmatter. At its best it may help us to develop a sound theory of science instruction which ignores neither the benefits of discovery (in the problem-solving sense) nor the necessity of firm content understanding.

David Hawkins has introduced a pleasantly descriptive term into the often inscrutable jargon of education. Taking the suggestion of the Water Rat in Kenneth Grahame's *The Wind in the Willows* that nothing is more worth doing than messing about in boats, Hawkins uses *messing about* in science education as a name for the completely unstructured (at least from the instructor's referent) way that children go about getting acquainted with materials when they are left alone.[9] Children so introduced to material are likely to allow the getting-acquainted process to lead them along different avenues of investigation. When this branching out takes place, Hawkins urges teachers to be ready to provide guidance along the various investigatory paths with "multiple programed" guides, that is, instruction tailored in advance to sustain investigation on a variety of topics. As an example, Hawkins lists eleven possible topics for investigation which could arise out of a child's initial acquaintance with a simple pendulum apparatus.[10] He suggests that the teacher could write open-ended guidance information on cards for each of these topics. A cross index of topics plus supplementary reading and audio-visual material would be available to the student after he is through messing about and ready to enter one area in depth. Lest this select against the more creative children, blank topic cards would be available for the inventive mind to lay bare its hitherto unimagined interests. Hawkins' ideal exercise terminates with a full-class discussion of "common elements" which are expressed with increased frequency as different investigations by different children proceed from initial messing about with identical materials. In such a discussion the whole class presents and argues over certain common elements which then may need a more formal attack, one at a time. Thus the following sequence exists, which terminates where conventional teaching often begins: messing about; multiple programming; full class discussion of commonness; formal hypothetic-deductive investigation of a single problem.[11] Hawkins' students all focus on one formal problem because they need to. Very often science

[9] David Hawkins, "Messing About in Science," *Science and Children*, Vol. 2 (February, 1965), pp. 5–9.

[10] Ibid, p. 8.

[11] Ibid., p. 9.

students so focus merely because the teacher or workbook tells them they must.

A class may not cover as much formal content in this unconventional way as another class whose teacher is not so "wasteful" of time as to allow messing about. But, then, the authors suggest that whoever was responsible for substituting the word *coverage* (usually coverage by the teacher) for *understanding* on the list of educational priorities cared little about educating children and cared less for the disciplined structure of knowledge which must, as in the case of any structure, be built with some kind of order. A teacher who covers content while serving as a slave to the table of contents, clock, and calendar is analogous to a building foreman who gives his carpenters and bricklayers only so much time for each floor before they must move on to the next. Imagine bricklayers standing on a scaffold attached to the third floor of a structure so built, while beating the clock to complete the fourth! Similarly, picture a class of children depending on previously "covered" content to support their efforts to understand what they are currently beating the bell to conquer. Who could condone such a building method, let alone live in such a building? In like manner, who could condone such teaching? Unfortunately, many teachers know no other way. Only a moment's review of the preceding analogy would suggest that such methodology is not efficient use of educational time and insults both the children and the discipline to which they are supposedly being exposed.

J. Richard Suchman holds that the most impressive precondition for inquiry is autonomy of the learner.[12] He has made self-direction a necessary part of inquiry. In his definition, inquiry occurs when conceptual reshaping results from the individual gathering and processing data himself.[13] Suchman views inquiry as being affected by psychological variables such as *styles* of thinking—for example, conceptual or cognitive style. Psychological studies by Kagan, Moss, and Sigel[14] have revealed that the criteria children use for categorizing objects (and, hence, the basic ways in which they organize impressions of their environment) are stylized and used with consistency by the individual child of prehigh school age. Recently studies by Scott and Sigel[15]

---

[12] J. Richard Suchman, "The Child and the Inquiry Process," in A. Harvey Passow, ed., *Intellectual Development* (Washington, D.C.: American Association for Supervision and Curriculum Development, 1964), cited in Raths, *Studying Teaching*, p. 275.

[13] Ibid., p. 262.

[14] Jerome Kagan, Howard Moss, and Irving E. Sigel, "Psychological Significance of Styles of Conceptualization," *Monographs of the Society for Research in Child Development*, Vol. 28 (1963), pp. 73–112.

[15] Norval C. Scott and Irving E. Sigel, *Effects of Inquiry Training in Physical Science on Creativity and Cognitive Styles of Elementary School Children* (Detroit: Merrill-Palmer Institute, 1965), 127 pp.

have found that change in style of classifying is contingent upon whether or not students are given inquiry training, and Koutnik[16] has found that success of fifth- and sixth-graders in solving certain kinds of electric circuit problems is contingent upon style of classifying. Scott has concluded that identifying eleven-year-old students' classification style is a better predictor of success on a test of science concept attainment than an I.Q. test.[17]

Three basic styles of classifying have been recognized in most of these studies: descriptive-analytic, which depends on observed or *manifest* attributes (for example, cars with four doors classified separately from two-door cars); categorical-inferential, which depends on *inferred* attributes (for example, plums, cherries, and peaches classified together because the presence of one inner seed is inferred although not seen in the case at hand); and relational, which depends upon some functional or thematic relationship between objects being classified (for example, a maid might be classified with a house because she is the cleaner of that particular house).

That something as ostensibly simple as a test to determine how pupils classify things can enable a prediction as to their success in a science learning situation is not so curious if we realize that classification styles (that is, styles of relating things to each other) will, in large part, determine how information will be linked together and stored in the mind for future retrieval.[18] A person of predominantly descriptive-analytic style preference may view a problematic situation in a different light from one who prefers relational or categorical-inferential criteria.

Suchman's inquiry-training project is of special interest here because it makes use of discrepancy.[19] In using inquiry training, the teacher provides the class with opportunities to observe happenings that are immediately inexplicable and that arouse curiosity. Two discrepant events are (1) a man boiling coffee and then drinking it as it continues to boil and (2) several men trying, with difficulty, to start a stalled car rolling whereas one man is able to maintain its movement, once started, with ease. Once focused by such teacher-provided events, the inquiry of students is allowed to range free, with the student gathering and processing information in accordance with his needs. While this is going on the teacher serves to provide any information asked

[16] Paul G. Koutnik, *The Effect of Cognitive Style, Sex and Degree of Completeness of an Electric Data Background on Student Prediction of Circuital Function*, unpublished doctoral dissertation, Indiana University, 1968.

[17] Norval C. Scott, "Science Concept Achievement Cognitive Functions," *Journal of Research in Science Teaching*, Vol. 2 (1964), pp. 7–16.

[18] Irvin E. Sigel, *Cognitive Style Test, Form A* (Detroit: 1967), 35 pp. (Available from the author at the Merrill-Palmer Institute; 71 E. Ferry; Detroit, Michigan.)

[19] Suchman, op. cit., p. 272.

for to keep things moving and keep the environment "responsive" and relatively free of frustration. One very important factor is the complete absence of extrinsic motivation. No searching for teacher or peer approval is encouraged. No search for what the teacher considers to be the "right answer" is allowed. Suchman depends on student motivation to close the gap created initially by the discrepancy, and with a lot of inquiry experience, the fun of inquiry action itself. He hopes that the child will first replace the need for "praise" with a need for "gap-closure" and eventually will replace this motivational form with a love of inquiry itself.[20]

Last in our brief survey of learning and instructional pretheory is a look at the work currently being done at one of eleven Regional Educational Laboratories set up under the Elementary and Secondary Education Act. The Mid-continent Regional Educational Laboratory (McREL) at Kansas City had, in the late 1960's, a major focus of self-directed learning and, within it, self-directed inquiry. Largely in agreement with Bruner's and Suchman's convictions relative to self-direction and inquiry, McREL had as its mission the definition, production, and measurement of self-directed inquiry and teacher-student inquiry skills in general. Programs under development at this laboratory have aimed not only at students but at pre- and in-service teachers as well. Both the student- and teacher-related work of the laboratory assumes that a way can be found to get students to *manage their own* inquiry learning. As might be expected, bits and pieces of a theory of instruction have been dropping out of various laboratory developmental programs. In the hope that the reader will be able to gather some of these bits and pieces and move closer to a theory of his own, McREL efforts in tenth-grade biology will be reviewed.

The Inquiry Role Approach (IRA) to biology seeks, over the span of the usual academic year, to move students from almost total dependence on their teacher for all directions to self-directed learners making their own decisions, designing their own instruction, participating in grading, and initiating and carrying out their own research. At the same time, the IRA program seeks to move teachers from the role of imparter of all significant information to that of manager of the self-instructional situation. Richard M. Bingman, one of the authors, and many biology teachers have been responsible for developing this effort in sixteen Kansas City high schools and other schools in and outside of the mid-continent region.

Early in the year IRA biology students are introduced to a discussion and laboratory procedure which involves taking defined roles. In four student teams these roles are *Team Coordinator*, or discussion leader and problem

---

[20] J. Richard Suchman, "The Illinois Studies in Inquiry Training," *Journal of Research in Science Teaching*, Vol. 2, No. 3 (1964), pp. 230–32.

clarifier; *Technical Adviser*, or reader and interpreter of materials and "main ideas" for the team (this role must also assume leadership in challenging assumptions made by the team and suggesting divergent ways of looking at a problem); *Data Recorder*, or summarizer of team decisions, who also determines sufficiency of evidence to support a team or member decision; *Process Adviser*, or recorder of problems in the area of role execution and social interaction (this role initiates discussions related to teamwork problems and provides initial suggestions for resolution of same). Laboratory activities call for other kinds of role differentiation with the emphasis on coordination of phases of lab work by the role takers, with all team members working together on specific tasks under a member's direction rather than "spreading out," as on an assembly line. These role descriptions are of key characteristics and do not encompass all behaviors that IRA students practice toward mastery. Charles Nelson (Associate Professor of Sociology at Indiana State University, Terre Haute, Indiana) led in developing the antecedents of these discussion roles and procedures by which the team members themselves can refine their role-related performance.

Often at first and steadily throughout their use, the roles are switched by the teacher. In addition, team makeup is periodically altered. This allows a student a broad acquaintance with classmates in different roles and enables him to sample all of the roles personally.

Basic to the Inquiry Role Approach is the use of Inquiry Guides. At first provided by the teacher and later in the year written by student teams themselves, these guides provide a focus for the content and process aims of a team. At this writing, all teacher-provided Inquiry Guides have been written by biology teachers and edited by McREL's IRA staff. The Lab considers this teacher writing involvement an important factor in changing the teacher's role in the classroom. Final packaging of the IRA program will include training materials for teacher writing of guide material rather than a completely polished assortment of activities. (Recall that teacher growth as a manager is a central part of the IRA program.) An example of an Inquiry Guide is provided in Figure 9-1.

In a typical use of an Inquiry Guide the teacher provides a copy of the Inquiry Guide to each student. Students then "work" it individually as homework. The routine is as follows. The student reads the materials listed as references. (To date, reference material has been limited mainly, for research and developmental convenience, to readings in BSCS texts and laboratory manuals. Further development will see the introduction here of other BSCS and non-BSCS biology literature.) He then reads the "Search for Concept" and stem. Often the stem is in the form of a situation. Stems give the student

Example: Inquiry Guide

Chapter 8

Search for Concept:

A forest community
in natural balance

A Middle Eastern American forest of spruce trees is also the nesting ground of a stable population of woodpeckers. The woodpeckers subsist on bark-boring beetle adults and larvae which they pick from the spruce bark surface and peck through the bark to find. The boring beetles are the major parasite of the spruce trees and make up the bulk of woodpecker food. The forest has been in a rather stable condition for over 200 years. Which of the following would be true of this forest situation?

Reference:
Yellow Version
pp. 160-177

Evidence:

A. _____ The spruce trees are first-order consumers.

B. _____ The woodpeckers are dependent on the spruce trees as a source of energy.

C. _____ Because the woodpeckers prey on the boring beetles, the spruce trees are dependent on the woodpeckers for survival.

D. _____ A sudden increase in the woodpecker population would have no effect on the spruce tree population.

E. _____ A sudden decrease in the tree population would have a great effect on boring beetle survival but little effect on woodpecker survival.

Summarize the main principle or concept presented here:

_____
_____
_____

Application question: Suppose a violent wind blew down a row of spruce trees. The fallen trees, with their tangled mass of branches pressed against the ground, now become a protective haven for boring beetles. The woodpeckers cannot get to the undersides of the bark through the tangled branches. What could be the consequence of this?

_____
_____
_____

Figure 9-1. IRA Inquiry Guide. (Reprinted with permission of Mid-continent Regional Educational Laboratory.)

instructions needed to complete the "guide." The student next reads the "inferences" (this logic term is used mainly to differentiate these tasks from "alternatives" of an objective test item) and marks each true or false. The task does not end here, however, as he must, when marking an "inference," list page, paragraph, and title of reference used in gathering evidence to support his true or false mark, *plus* write a short statement of the evidence in his own words. Anything less will not count. Unfounded guesswork is, thus, discouraged, and the informed opinion is rewarded. Finally, the student must summarize the major concept or *overall idea* which the stem and "inferences" were getting at and answer a terminal question which requires application of this "overall idea" beyond text and Inquiry-Guide contexts.

Next day in class the student gives his individual work to his teacher and sits in his role-differentiated team while all members "butt heads" to arrive at some combination of consensus and dissension over the propriety of answers and evidence. The small team gives each member a chance to have his say and both give and take criticism under the scrutiny of the Data Recorder, who checks against the printed word, and other role takers, who work together to develop a value for "best evidence" and finally summarize team output in a more polished, team-worked Inquiry Guide.

In the last fifteen or twenty minutes of the class period the teacher calls all teams together to read and challenge each other's output. Thus ideas and information go through three levels of conceptualization and refinement. The first level is a result of individual work. The second level results from the cumulative effect of individual plus group work, and the third results from individual plus group plus whole class discussion. The McREL staff feels that text, lab, and other materials are being used as reference and support for decision making rather than as input for role memorization or wholly directed activities.

While teams are working independently of each other, the teacher has a unique opportunity to visit individual teams, study the learning process, and clinic the interactive ills of students involved in a critical review. All of this may add to the effectiveness of the teacher's role in the final whole-class discussion when he enters discussion with recent knowledge of the problems, successes, and directions of teams' searches for understanding beforehand.

A second part of an Inquiry Guide is its Teacher-Communication Sheet. A sheet for the previously illustrated guide is presented in Figure 9-2.

Any given Inquiry-Guide–Teacher-Communication-Sheet combination is written as a unit roughly as follows. A major concept (principle) is selected. Then at least five content subconcepts (column 1) or subordinate principles are derived from it. Then the writer determines some level (column 2) of

Teacher Communication Sheet

Chapters 1, 2, and 3 Green

A Forest Community in Natural Balance

Content Subconcepts	*Student Behavior Elicited*	*Possible Student Evidence*
A. Chlorophyllous plants are producers in a community. Organisms feeding on producers are first-order consumers.	*Recognizes* an organism as a green plant and classifies it as a producer.	**(F)** Spruce trees are green plants, and so must be producers rather than consumers.
B. Organisms in a community have indirect energy relationships via other organisms. Or, producers constitute the energy basis of a community.	*Analyzes* relationships between organisms to reveal indirect dependence. Or applies knowledge that green plants are ultimately the source of a community's energy.	**(T)** Woodpeckers (consumers) get energy from the beetles (consumers), which, in turn, get it from the trees (producers). Therefore, woodpeckers are indirectly dependent on the trees for energy. *or:* Spruce trees as producers are ultimately energy providers for the rest of the community.
C. One population in a community is dependent for its maintenance on populations which may be one or more energy levels removed.	*Comprehends* an example of indirect dependence.	**(T)** This follows from the stem. Could be reinforced by evidence from any text discussion of food webs and/or population homeostasis. Summary of analogy to room temperature. **(C)**
D. Sudden population size fluctuations in a given trophic level may be echoed throughout a community because of interrelationships.	*Analyzes* relationships between organisms to reveal indirect dependence, and *predicts* effects on one population when others are manipulated.	**(F)** Food web principles (Chapter 1), analogy and example from 60–61 (Chapter 2), and integration of material from 83–89 (Chapter 3).
E. (Same as above)	(Same as above)	**(F)** (Similar to above)

Figure 9-2. IRA Teacher Communication Sheet. (Reprinted with permission of Mid-continent Regional Educational Laboratory.)

understanding at which each subconcept should be internalized such that internalization of all five at their respective levels will give the student an ability to understand the major concept at least at the level of application.[21] Next (or often hand in hand with the preceding steps) a stem and the Inquiry-Guide inferences are written so that the student can understand the content subconcepts at a given level. Finally, the third column of evidences is written. When empirically validated by the teacher in the classroom, this last column may be refined to approach not only evidence as the student sees it for a true or a false inference, but evidence for the teacher that a content subconcept has been learned at near an intended level of understanding. (The reader may see in this system a resemblance to performance objectives.) The Inquiry-Guide and Teacher-Communication-Sheet system of planning for individual and team instruction is an extension of the performance objective system, with the Guide serving as a situation, columns 2 and 3 serving as performance term and qualifier.

There is no set formula of so many true to so many false inferences. When one sees inferences as representative of a subconceptual association of learnings, all of whose members are important to an understanding of a larger whole, considerations of numbers false, or "distractors," become irrelevant.

Inquiry Guides, as provided for in IRA, deepen in complexity and come more and more to represent inquiry situations rather than direct "book comprehension."

At a time when mastery of provided materials is judged adequate and students are flexible and task oriented in their teams, the teacher introduces to teams the task of preparing actual Inquiry Guides and Teacher Communication Sheets themselves. Students' products are tried on the class and criticized by the students themselves. Further research will show whether or not students consider this to be a significant change in instructional decision-making authority.

At this point in the IRA, students are allowed to discuss original papers in biology, some of which are student authored and some of which are not. The goal here is to develop a criterial bias in line with scientific objectivity. Criticism alone is cheap, but criticism founded on objective internal and external criteria is a special skill worth developing for biology, school, and life. Guidelines laid down by a BSCS–McREL team are used in this part of the IRA.[22]

[21] Benjamin Bloom (ed.), *The Taxonomy of Educational Objectives*, Handbook I (New York: David McKay, 1956), pp. 201–207.

[22] Richard Bingman (ed.), *Inquiry Objectives in the Teaching of Biology*, McREL Position Paper, Vol. 1, No. 1 (September, 1969). Biological Science Curriculum Study and Mid-continent Regional Educational Laboratory; 104 East Independence Avenue; Kansas City, Missouri 64106.

Finally, after gradually having gained direction of their learning while they were developing content understanding and critical thinking skills, the students are turned loose in class to select and go as far as they are able with a biology problem. They may choose to work alone or with others. They will evaluate each other's reports. At this stage the teacher is serving mainly as a resource person on call and as a participant-observer in the evaluation process.

The development of the IRA program has followed an eclectic course with respect to learning theory and instructional variables described in the literature review section of this chapter. With proper design the IRA program may be seen as a testing ground for learning and instructional hypotheses both new and old.

Other developmental programs at McREL aimed at self-direction in biology classes assume that if the teacher has nearly immediate knowledge of the relationship between his verbal input and the discussion paths taken afterward by his students, he can test antecedent–consequent hypotheses about verbal interaction. After he sees that his words can affect class output, he can come to control his speech, use discussion skills, and actually set performance objectives in terms of desired specific student verbal output. One such project, Instructional Staff Development, a cooperative venture between McREL and University of Nebraska's Teachers College, holds these interaction analysis[23] assumptions and attempts to develop the equivalent of our previously mentioned hypothesizing teacher whose goal is, in this case, student centeredness[24] and finally true student self-direction of inquiry.

From this cursory review it may seem that there is little specific agreement about how to go about developing a theory of instruction for science. Many people place high value on inquiry or problem solving, but an equal number disagree as to the extent that and means by which these goals may be reached. There are those who challenge the notion of learning how to learn. Others, of course, accept the notion as valid. But common points exist in the various attempts to make science teaching more of an applied subject and less of an art form for a talented few.

The principles of structure of knowledge, the personal nature of coming to know a thing, and our acceptance of empiricism itself as a *means* toward building a theory as well as the very *philosophy* we are trying to bring science students to value are some points generally agreed on. At least we are consistent in the latter case. Finally, some form of idiosyncratic synthesis or

---

[23] See pp. 16–26 of this text.

[24] This is a midpoint on a theoretical model of teacher growth between the extremes of total teacher direction and total student direction. At this point, teacher and students equally share responsibility for setting goals of planning.

relationship construction is pictured variously as discovery, problem solving, or inquiry. All are not agreed on the extent to which the teacher should direct instruction but writings on personal knowledge and inquiry lead us to suspect that a theory of science instruction will involve the teacher as little as is needed to enable students to work without the teacher. Another thing is especially clear from the work of Hawkins, Gagné, and the McREL staff, which is that teachers will need to be planners par excellence. Theories deriving from the personal involvement with materials, the structure of knowledge, the desirability of totally self-directed inquiry, or any mixture of these issues will require for their application the careful situation setting and long-term planning of a hypothesizing teacher who will know the limits within which to play causal games. Every instance of his hypothesizing will become a test of the theory from which he is deriving his causes.

Discussion Questions

1. Select one of the instructional theorists named earlier in this chapter and explore some experimental or curricular papers written by him. Report on one of these to your class or group and comment on the relevance of the paper to improving science instruction.
2. Educationists are accused from time to time of being too theoretical. If they are, we would not have needed to write this chapter: true or false? Explain your answer.
3. How do *you* approach problems or learning in general? Compare your approach to conditions and structure that Bruner, Gagné, Hawkins, and Suchman use to describe optimum learning. Which writer's ideas would be most relevant for someone to be aware of if he were your teacher?

Additional References[25]

Brakken, E. "Inquiry Involves Individualizing," *Instructor*, Vol. 78 (October, 1968).

[25] The following film and materials may be of use to pre- and in-service science teachers and their instructors:

Film:
  Learning Through Inquiry; Institute for Development of Educational Activities, Inc., an affiliate of the Charles F. Kettering Foundation, Suite 300, 5335 Far Hills Avenue, Dayton, Ohio 45429.

Materials:
  Biological Sciences Curriculum Study. A list of publications and films on inquiry methodology, rationale, and evaluations is available on request. P.O. Box 930, Boulder, Colorado 80302.

  Management Research Associates, Charles Nelson, Director. A list of publications on organizational and staff development is available from this firm. 185 N. Wabash, Chicago, Illinois.

  McREL. A list of current inquiry development publications is available from Midcontinent Regional Educational Laboratory, 104 East Independence Avenue, Kansas City, Missouri 64106.

Butts, D. P. "The Relationship of Problem Solving Ability and Science Knowledge," *Science Education*, Vol. 49 (March, 1965), pp. 138–146.

Butts, D. P., and H. L. Jones. "Inquiry Training and Problem Solving in Elementary School Children," *Journal of Research in Science Teaching* (1966).

Craig, R. C. "Recent Research on Discovery," *Educational Leadership*, Vol. 26 (February, 1969).

Dickinson, M. B. *Independent and Group Learning*. Washington, D.C.: National Educational Association, n.d.

Gagné, R. M., and L. T. Brown. "Some Factors in the Programming of Conceptual Learning," *Journal of Experimental Psychology*, Vol. 62 (October, 1961).

Science Education Information Analysis Center. *Science Education Information Report: Bibliography 1, Instructional Procedures*. Columbus: Ohio State University, 1967.

programed and computerized instruction*

An Overview of the Programing Process

What Is Programed Instruction?

A program is an instructional sequence designed to help the student attain certain specific objectives which have been formulated from an analysis of the task. The instructional material has been modified on the basis of student tryouts, and the final version is accompanied by validation data describing the performance of a specified group of students who have completed the program.[1]

This comprehensive definition can be applied to *all* programed materials, including programed movies, programed filmstrips, and programed group discussions. These will be discussed in detail later in this chapter. Most familiar are programed textbooks, which are usually broken down into discrete units of information called frames. There are five possible parts in each frame

* Prepared by James D. Russell, Department of Biological Science, Purdue University.

The author wishes to express his sincere gratitude to Sivasailam Thiagarajan, programed instruction specialist, and to Dr. Arthur Babick, computerized instruction specialist. Without the complete assistance of these educators and friends it would have been impossible to assemble the material contained in this chapter. A special thanks to my wife, Nancy, for editing the mountains of manuscript from which this chapter took its final form.

[1] S. Thiagarajan, James Russell, and Arthur Babick, *Programed Programing* (Bloomington, Ind.: Thiagarajan, 1970).

Here is a rapid method for multiplying any number by 11

Step 1: Place a zero in front of the number and another zero behind it.

Step 2: Starting with the last digit of the original number, add each digit to its right-hand neighbor.

Step 3: Put down each of the above sums in front of one another.

Information

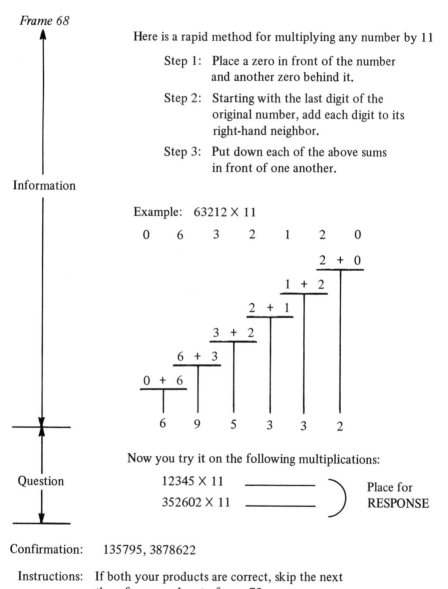

Example: 63212 × 11

Now you try it on the following multiplications:

Question

12345 × 11 ——————
352602 × 11 ——————

Place for RESPONSE

Confirmation: 135795, 3878622

Instructions: If both your products are correct, skip the next three frames and go to frame 72.

Figure 10-1. Sample frame.

—information, question, place for response, confirmation of response (correct or suggested answer), and instructions. However, depending upon the specific purpose of the frame and the nature of the program, all five parts need not be present in *each* frame. Refer to the sample frame in Figure 10-1.

First, some *information* in printed form, diagrams, or photographs is presented to the student. The amount and complexity of this information should depend upon the students for which the program has been designed. Then a *question* directs the student's attention to the most critical information presented, or a question may require the student to apply a principle learned from the frame. A place for the student's response is provided. Usually he is required actually to record his answer, or he may be requested to perform certain manipulations with equipment. By moving a cover sheet down the page, by turning the page, or by referring to a confirmation booklet, the student is informed of the correct answer, or he is given a model answer for comparison. Finally, *instructions* are given directing the student to the next frame. He may be told to skip the next three frames, to go back to a previous frame, or to redo the last four frames. If the student is to progress in a serial sequence, the instructions are usually provided at the beginning of the sequence directing him to answer the frames in the order in which they appear in the book.

How Are Programs Designed and Developed?

Analyzing the Task and Stating Objectives

The typical process by which instructional programs are designed, developed, and validated is outlined in Figure 10-2. (Refer to it frequently during the following discussion.) The programer may or may not be familiar with the subject matter to be programed. Suppose you were asked to prepare a program on rheology. You do not know anything about the subject, except you have a vague idea that it may have something to do with rays. To overcome your deficiency in this subject-matter area, you could read books on rheology and take pertinent courses until you were adequately informed, or you could consult subject-matter specialists regarding various aspects of the topic to be programed.

From discussions with a subject-matter specialist or seeing a demonstration of the task, the programer can analyze the task to be programed. Then he must construct an extensive list of performance objectives in behavioral terms that specify what the student should be able to do as a result of the instruction. (See Chapter 5, p. 50, on stating objectives.) Specific objectives for any task can be obtained by dividing the overall task into a number of subtasks. For example, the objectives for a program on the operation of a binocular microscope may include the subtasks of carrying and handling the scope, preparing a slide for viewing, making coarse adjustments, making fine adjustments, and cleaning and maintaining the apparatus.

The list of performance objectives prepared as a result of the task analysis should be reviewed by the subject-matter specialist to ensure technical accuracy and completeness. Refer to the arrows in the Task Analysis section of Figure 10-2. The arrow labeled *no go* indicates that the subject-matter specialist did *not* approve the objectives, and they are returned to the programer for revisions. The arrow labeled *go* indicates that the objectives have been approved, and the programer moves to the next stage of the programing process.

Designing the Initial Version

The design stage is usually divided into three substages. Using the specific objectives as his guide, the programer first constructs questions that will determine if those objectives have been met. Three test items of equal difficulty are usually designed for each objective. One of these items is used in the pretest, another for the posttest, and a third is embedded in the instructional sequence to check the student's achievement as he proceeds through the program. After designing the test items, the programer prepares the instructional sequence. Finally, the programer must collect or prepare the adjunct materials which include specimens and diagrams or photographs to be examined, models to be used, and equipment to be manipulated, such as laboratory apparatus.

During the design stage the programer prepares a "rough draft" of his program. He then revises and rewrites the material until he is satisfied. The arrow marked *not satisfied* in Figure 10-2 indicates that more revisions are to be undertaken by the programer. When he is satisfied, the rough draft becomes the initial version of the program, and it then moves on to the next stage of the process.

Editing

The initial version of the program should be carefully edited. A subject-matter specialist can correct subject-matter inaccuracies. Another programer should read the material and suggest ways to improve the programing format. Finally, a language specialist should read the material, improve the writing

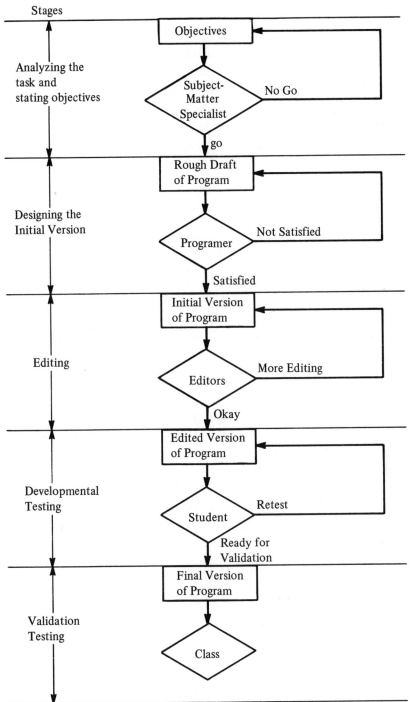

Stages

Analyzing the task and stating objectives

Objectives

Subject-Matter Specialist → No Go

go

Designing the Initial Version

Rough Draft of Program

Programer → Not Satisfied

Satisfied

Editing

Initial Version of Program

Editors → More Editing

Okay

Developmental Testing

Edited Version of Program

Student → Retest

Ready for Validation

Validation Testing

Final Version of Program

Class

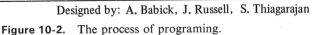

Designed by: A. Babick, J. Russell, S. Thiagarajan

Figure 10-2. The process of programing.

style, and correct errors in grammar, spelling, and punctuation. The initial version continues to be edited (see Figure 10-2) until all subject-matter, programing, and language errors have been corrected; then it becomes the edited version and moves to the next stage of programing.

Developmental Testing

The purpose of developmental testing is to maximize the program's effectiveness. A student from the population for which the program was designed goes through the edited version while the programer observes him closely, analyzing the student's reactions, his responses to each frame, and his comments. On the basis of this data and the student's posttest results, inefficient areas of the program can be located. A single tryout with a representative student helps to pinpoint problem areas for that one particular student, but there may be other weak areas which would be obvious to a different student. In addition, the revisions based on testing with one student might create new problems for other students. Therefore, such revisions are tested again with another student. The cycle of testing revision, retesting, and revision is continued until the material proves its effectiveness. (See Figure 10-2.) Then the program is ready to be validated.

Validation Testing

The purpose of validation testing is to *demonstrate* the effectiveness of an instructional program. Students who have completed the program are tested to determine their achievement. Complete validation studies should include

1. Increase in student achievement.
2. Changes in interest in subject matter.
3. Changes in attitude toward programed instruction.
4. Efficiency of instruction (amount learned/time).

Even after the program has been validated by extensive testing, the classroom teacher needs to monitor the performance of the students working with the material and make necessary revisions if the students do not meet the objectives of the program.

Principles of Programed Learning

Now that we have become aware of the process of programing, let us look at some of the educational principles underlying programed learning which make this strategy a valuable classroom technique.

1. *Goal-oriented learning.* A program helps the student acquire specific knowledge or skills. All trivial, irrelevant, and superfluous material is excluded.
2. *Logical sequence.* In programed instruction the steps are organized in an "optimum" order. The programer spends many hours analyzing the task or concept to be learned. As a result of this extensive analysis, each frame is related to those which precede and follow it. For science topics a hierarchy is usually the most logical sequence.
3. *Optimum step size.* Rather than requesting the student to digest large amounts of material, such as a chapter in a textbook, programed instruction breaks the material into smaller, more digestible pieces. Educators have consistently disagreed regarding optimum frame size, or more explicity, whether large "chunks" can be digested as easily as small bits. Some believe the amount of information presented should be very small (twenty-five to fifty words); others state emphatically that the quantity of material per frame should be much larger (at least a paragraph or two). Today most programers have compromised and hold that the optimum step size depends upon the nature of the content, as well as upon the students for whom it is designed. Uniform step size need not be used throughout the entire program.
4. *Active participation.* Most programers agree that students are more likely to learn what they experience firsthand; that is, learning results from active involvement. A teacher can expose students to textbooks, lectures, or films to which the students may not respond. But in programed instruction, the student responds to the material in every frame. Consequently, he becomes actively involved throughout the learning process. Active responding requires and maintains student attention.
5. *Immediate confirmation of results.* The program reinforces or corrects the student's response immediately. As soon as the student responds, he turns the page, moves a slider, or refers to a confirmation booklet to determine whether he is right or wrong. The confirmation reinforces the response and makes it more probable that the student will respond similarly in future situations. In contrast, when the teacher administers a test, the student is usually not informed of the accuracy of his performance for several days.
6. *Self-pacing.* The student is allowed to proceed at his own rate. The faster students are not restrained, nor are the slower ones rushed through material they do not understand. Because each student has

his own program, his ability to perform determines his rate of progress. Other instructional techniques, such as the traditional lecture or film, require each student to proceed at the same rate. Some are bored, others are lost. "Individual differences" are not new in science education, but programed instruction takes advantage of them, thereby renewing the educator's awareness of their importance.

7. *Programs are tested and validated.* The guiding principle of programed instruction today is testing and validation. The programer has not finished his task until he can say "yes" to the question, "Does it work?" Unfortunately, many of the early programs (and even some today) have not been validated. Therefore, it is the responsibility of every teacher who is interested in using an instructional program to request the validation data from the publisher. If these data are not available, the teacher should be suspicious of the material; perhaps it is just another text disguised as a "program."

Advantages and Disadvantages of Programed Instruction

Programed instruction has been called the most exciting advance in learning technology in recent years. Perhaps a look at some of its advantages and disadvantages will increase our understanding of this new educational technique.

The emphasis of programed instruction is on learning rather than on teaching. The activities of the student are directed, not the activities of the teacher. The teacher's function becomes one of prescriber, motivator, and resource person. Programing is student centered. Early in the development of programed instruction it was recognized that, unlike a lecture or film, programed materials can be adjusted to each individual's rate of learning. However, individualizing instruction can pose a serious problem, namely, determining the individual student's needs, interests, abilities, and aptitudes. Because this requires extensive testing and diagnostic study, measuring instruments need to be developed to examine the individual more thoroughly and more objectively. It is possible, however, to use a variety of programs with different approaches to meet the same objectives, thus capturing the interest and meeting the needs of a greater number of students.

Programed sequences have been shown to reduce the amount of time required to meet prestated objectives. This raises the question of what students who finish a program do while the other students are still working. Scheduling can create complex administrative problems which must be solved within both the individual classroom and the entire school. Classroom management is one of the teacher's biggest problems when using programed materials. One solution is to use a completely individualized pattern in which the student is allowed to work through the program and take the appropriate criterion tests at any time he wishes. Another is the partially individualized pattern in which the student is on a fixed schedule for completing each unit of the program but in which he may study the material whenever he chooses. Under no circumstances should a student be assigned a minimum amount of material to be covered within a single class period.

The applicability of programed instruction to wide ability and age ranges is advantageous. Programed materials have been used successfully from the elementary school through adult education in almost every subject-matter field, including all areas of science and mathematics. Programing instruction can end the traditional subject-matter assignment according to the chronological age of the student. Tenth-grade biology students can use materials formerly taught only in an advanced course. With programed materials it is easier to expand the curriculum to include courses to be taken by a few students or courses for which there is no teacher. This is an important consideration, especially for smaller schools.

When compared with most textbooks, programed materials are usually more effective and they have the advantage of thorough validation testing. However, programed materials require much time and effort to develop; consequently, they are more expensive than traditional textbooks. The increased efficiency of this approach to learning tends to compensate for higher costs. Programs also provide for increased flexibility in the science curriculum. By using programed units which are shorter than conventional textbooks, the teacher can structure a course to meet both the needs and interests of the students and his own requirements. Properly planned, a programed approach not only effectively utilizes instructional materials, but also permits the most efficient use of teaching and learning time. Programed materials can also add variety to the classroom activities. It should be emphasized that programed instruction is still only *one* of the tools of science education.

Opponents of programed instruction imply that this technique is "dehumanizing education." They maintain that programs do not permit valuable student interaction because the students are rarely at the same frame simultaneously. However, individualized instruction does not mean that the students are always working alone. Activities can be programed for group participation. The technique of programed group discussions will be presented later in this chapter. Programs also release the teacher from routine instruction to interact individually with students and to provide human reinforcement.

The diverse applications of programed materials are advantageous to the science teacher. Programs can provide regular instruction, enrichment instruction, remedial instruction, and absentee instruction in addition to establishing prerequisite competencies for science courses.

Our discussion thus far has been an overview of the programing process. Perhaps you are now interested in how it all began.

Programing Fundamentals

Origin of Teaching Machines and Programed Instruction

Early in the development of programed instruction, the emphasis was on the use of machines. One type of teaching machine was developed during the 1920's by S. L. Pressey.[2] Pressey's primary concerns were to administer and to score multiple-choice tests. He later discovered an extension of his machine—self-instruction. Because his "teaching machine" was a testing device, the machine "program" was intended to supplement the textbook, and not to replace it.

Linear Formats

B. F. Skinner developed an entirely different type of teaching machine during the mid-1950's as a means of implementing operant conditioning principles in the classroom.[3] Skinner believed that reinforcement was the *primary* basis of all learning; therefore, by using small steps in each frame, the student was more likely to give consistently correct responses, and this success would reinforce him. From Skinner's experimental work with teaching machines evolved the *linear program*, which can be represented diagrammatically as shown in Figure 10-3.

What are the characteristics of a linear program? Each student follows the *same path* through the program. The pieces of information presented (steps or frames) are small, usually a sentence or two. A constructed response is required, recalling and actually writing the answer, rather than selecting or recognizing the correct response from several alternatives. Linear programers attempt to eliminate student errors, because the student may "learn" the

---

[2] S. L. Pressey, "A Simple Apparatus Which Gives Tests and Scores—and Teaches," *School and Society*, Vol. 23 (1926), pp. 373–76.

[3] B. F. Skinner, "Teaching Machines," *Science*, Vol. 128 (1958), pp. 969–77.

17   An electron has one unit of *negative* electric charge.
A proton has one unit of *positive* electric charge.
A neutron has no electric charge at all.

The atom as a whole is neutral. It does not have any
electric charge because the negative charges are
exactly cancelled by the positive charges.

Therefore, there should be an equal number of   electrons
_____ and _____   protons
in an atom.   (either order)

18   An atom of carbon has 6 protons in its nucleus. How
many electrons revolve around this nucleus?

_____.   6

19   The mass of a proton is used as the unit for measuring
the masses of atoms. Neutrons have a mass equal to
that of a proton. The mass of an electron is so small,
in comparison with that of a proton, that it is not taken
into account at all.

The mass of a carbon atom is 12 units. It has 6 protons.
How many neutrons does it have? _____.   6

20   This is a symbolic representation of a nitrogen atom.
The first number, called the atomic number,

     14   represents the number of electrons in
     N   the atom. The second number, called
     7   the mass number, indicates the total
         mass of the atom.

How many of each of the following subatomic
particles does nitrogen have?   7,7,7
Electrons _____, Protons _____, Neutrons _____.

Figure 10-3. Excerpt from a Linear Program, *Atoms and Molecules*, Sivasailam
Thiagarajan. (Reprinted by permission of the author.)

wrong answer by writing it. Therefore, linear programers strive for a minimum of 95 per cent correct responses.

Branching Formats

The branching or intrinsic programing format, usually associated with Norman A. Crowder, presents an interesting contrast to the linear program.[4] Refer to the sample branching program excerpt in Figure 10-4. How can

38.

Solid	Volume of Solid	Liquid	Weight of Solid		Loss of Weight
			in Air	in Liquid	
Iron	10 cc	water	79 g	69 g	10 g
Iron	20 cc	water	158 g	138 g	20 g
Iron	10 cc	kerosene	79 g	71 g	8 g
Iron	20 cc	kerosene	158 g	142 g	16 g
Gold	10 cc	water	197 g	187 g	10 g
Gold	20 cc	water	394 g	374 g	20 g
Gold	10 cc	kerosene	197 g	189 g	8 g
Gold	20 cc	kerosene	394 g	378 g	16 g

Study this table carefully.

It shows that when a solid is completely immersed in a liquid, there is an apparent loss of weight. This loss of weight depends on

the nature of the solid and of the liquid . . . . . . go to frame 39

the volume of the solid and the nature of the liquid . . go to frame 40

the weight of the solid in air . . . . go to frame 41

Figure 10-4. Portion of branching program by S. Thiagarajan. (Reprinted by permission of the author.)

[4] N. A. Crowder, "Automatic Tutoring by Means of Intrinsic Programing," in E. Glanter (ed.), *Automatic Teaching: The State of the Art* (New York: Wiley, 1959), pp. 109–116.

39.

Wrong!

You said that the loss of weight depends on the nature of the solid and of the liquid.

Study this part of the table carefully:

Iron	10 cc	water	79 g	69 g	10 g
Gold	10 cc	water	197 g	187 g	10 g

Notice that even when the nature of the solid changes, there is no difference in the loss of weight.

Return to frame 38 and make another choice.

40.

Correct!

The loss of weight depends on the volume of the solid and the nature of the liquid.

The density of water is 1 g/cc. when a solid of 10 cc is immersed in water, it loses 10 g.

The density of kerosene is .8 g/cc. When a solid of 10 cc is immersed in kerosene, it loses 8 g.

The density of salt solution is 1.2 g/cc. When a solid of 10 cc is immersed in salt solution, it would lose _____ g.

1.2 g	. . . .	frame 42
12 g	. . . .	frame 43
10 g	. . . .	frame 44
8 g	. . . .	frame 45

41.

Wrong!

You said that the loss of weight depends on the weight of the solid in air. This is not completely true.

Study this part of the table carefully:

Iron	10 cc	water	79 g	69 g	10 g
Iron	10 cc	kerosene	79 g	71 g	8 g

Notice that even though the weight of the solid in air is the same in both cases, there is a difference in the loss of weight.

Return to Frame 38 and choose a better answer.

Figure 10-4—*continued*.

intrinsic programing be characterized? A branching program might be represented diagrammatically as follows:

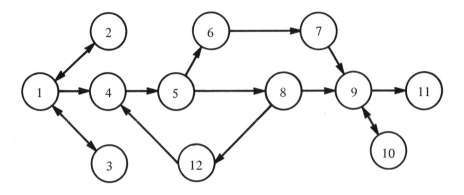

The program provides *different paths* for each student, depending upon his responses to the questions contained within the frames. Because the responses are usually *multiple-choice*, recognition of the correct answer rather than a constructed response is required. Instead of avoiding student errors with small linear steps, the branching format *utilizes* student errors in a diagnostic manner and thereby directs students to material designed to correct any misunderstandings.

Application of Programing Principles

Texts and Courses

In addition to textbook applications, the programing process can be used in the development of entire courses. The first programed courses developed were in the sciences, and they were not small-step, fill-in-the-blank, or scrambled books; rather, they were materials which had a set of specific behavioral objectives, had been tested and revised on the basis of student reaction, and were accompanied by validation data. The first of these courses was the high school physics course developed by the Physical Science Study Committee. The PSSC material was soon followed by BSCS Chem-Study, and Chem-Bond. The Earth Science Curriculum project is another example of a programed course. One of the most recent and most extensive of all the programed courses is the one generated by Harvard Project Physics. A team of physicists and educators from many parts of the country joined forces in July of 1964 and began spelling out the objectives of the course. That summer they generated material for experimental use in fifteen high schools with over

500 students during the 1964–1965 school year. The materials underwent four years of development, testing, and revision with over 10,000 students. The final version of the Project Physics course is accompanied by extensive validation data based upon student achievement, attitudes, intelligence, personality, prior achievement, and interest in science.

Film and Filmstrips

The programing process is also applicable to movies and filmstrips. To date, most programed films are in the area of education, and most of these deal with programed instruction, such as "Programing Is a Process" by Susan M. Markle and Philip W. Tiemann of the Office of Instructional Resources, University of Illinois at Chicago Circle and "Performance Objectives" by James Popham of the University of California at Los Angeles. Programed films and filmstrips are usually accompanied with a student-response sheet. During the presentation the students are requested to respond to stimulus material presented by the film.

If the objectives are explicit, a large-group lecture can be transformed into a programed film. The initial version would probably be in "story board" format (a series of drawings). After editing and refinement the material could be video-taped and subsequently tested with individual students or groups of students. The video tape allows for easy and inexpensive revision. Therefore, only after thorough developmental testing and revision in the video-tape format should the program be put on film, which is more permanent and more expensive. Because technical excellence is often confused with instructional efficiency, and because of the time, effort, and cost invested in producing professional-looking material, many programers tend to be reluctant to revise their products even when developmental testing suggests the need for modifications. Consequently, it has been recommended that validation data be compiled on the final video-tape version before making the filmed version. If the data meet the programer's criteria, then the film should be produced and validated, to be certain the instructional quality has been maintained.

Laboratories

In 1961 S. N. Postlethwait at Purdue University began using audio tapes as a means of programing instruction in his college botany course.[5] The

---

[5] S. N. Postlethwait, J. Novak, and H. Murray, *The Audio-Tutorial Approach to Learning* (Minneapolis: Burgess Publishing Company, 1969).

method included the development of a learning center with individual study carrels equipped with audio-tape playback machines, 8-mm projectors, as many of the actual objects studied as possible, and any additional materials needed for the unit of study. "Conventional" lectures, laboratories, and discussion sections have been eliminated in Postlethwait's course. Instead individualized instruction, observation of materials, and experimentation are provided in the study carrels or are made available at the demonstration areas in the learning center. An instructor is always nearby to answer specific questions. This programed college botany course provides uniform instruction for a large number of students and is available on an individual basis, allowing each student to study at a pace and time most convenient and effective for him. The student paces his study according to his ability to assimilate the information. Exposure to difficult subjects can be repeated as often as necessary. Each student is permitted to select a time for listening when he believes his study will be most efficient. The tapes actively involve the student and minimize distractions. Because the lessons are recorded on tape, make-up labs and review sessions are easily arranged with a minimum of effort. Postlethwait's audio-tutorial approach has also proved to be effective in teaching high school science courses.

Programed Group Discussions

Unfortunately many science educators have failed to recognize the learning potential inherent in small groups of six to ten students. They have conducted large-group instruction, such as lectures; they have used individual students in problem-solving situations and pairs of students in laboratory exercises, but the small group has not found its place in most science classrooms. An effective new teaching strategy for group learning has been developed at Indiana University under the direction of Sivasailam Thiagarajan and James Russell. The name *Grouprogram* has been coined for this novel approach which applies the principles of programed instruction to a group discussion. It utilizes many of the characteristics of conventional programed learning: specification of objectives, active participation, immediate confirmation, revision on the basis of student tryout and validation.

In a programed group discussion a reporter is chosen prior to each topic to record the main points discussed by his group, and another person is appointed discussion leader. The group leaders and reporters are selected by a random process, such as drawing cards, using the youngest person, using the tallest person, and so on. Each group leader begins the discussion, encourages all members to participate, and is in charge of the pace of the discussion. The reporter selected for each question summarizes his group's discussion and submits a brief report to the instructor at the next class meeting. These reports allow the teacher to monitor the progress of each group, even when he is not present for the discussion.

Because group discussions can easily drift into "tangent talk," it becomes necessary to limit the discussion time and to direct the students' attention to four or five specific questions which cover the more important skills and knowledge to be learned. An audio tape accomplishes these goals in the grouprogram. In addition, the selection of group leaders and reporters, an explanation of the topics to be discussed, and the timing of the discussion are handled effectively by the tape. For example, the tape may proceed as follows, "During this discussion your leader will be the person with the Jack of Diamonds and your reporter will be the person with the King of Clubs. Today we will discuss the plans to build a new canal between the Atlantic and Pacific Oceans. This canal will *not* prevent the mixing of the two oceans. List significant ecological consequences that could result." The tape indicates, "You will have fifteen minutes for this discussion." The tape also serves as a timing device and later warns, "You have one more minute to complete the discussion of this topic and to summarize your conclusions for the reporter." At the end of each discussion question model responses are provided for comparison with the group's conclusions.

The grouprogram using interaction among its group members can achieve complex objectives, such as "critical thinking," hypothesis formation, problem solving, and interpersonal skills. Structured group discussions benefit from the motivational effects of social reinforcement within the group. Observations of heterogeneous groups using grouprograms indicate that below-average participants are tutored by others in the group and consequently achieve higher levels of understanding; at the same time, the above-average students are given an opportunity to apply their knowledge to new situations, thus promoting a common level of understanding among the group members.

Teaching Machines and Machine Formats

Thus far we have discussed the techniques of programing—linear, branching, or a combination of the two. We have also learned how programed instruction can be applied to multiple learning media, such as textbooks, entire courses, films, and group discussions. In this section we will discuss other means by which the information in the frames can be presented to the student. The program presentation device is usually referred to as a *teaching machine*. The teaching machine is a mechanical, electrical, or electronic device which controls the presentation of the frames, keeps a record of the student's answers, and/or provides immediate feedback by displaying the correct answer. It must be emphasized that the educational value of a teaching machine depends entirely upon the quality of the program it presents.

Teaching machines vary in complexity and cost. At one end of the continuum are the relatively simple, mechanically operated machines which use programs printed on paper. The very complex electronic computer systems that use cathode-ray tubes for display purposes and electronic typewriters for input and output represent the opposite extreme. Most teaching machines tend to be nothing more than fancy, and expensive, "page turners." They can achieve no more than programed books achieve, yet involve a higher initial outlay and additional maintenance expense. As one teacher so aptly put it, "Books are cheaper, but they wear out rather quickly. Machines that break down wear out the teacher."

Machines do have the ability to control subsidiary equipment, such as tape recorders, slide projectors, film-loop projectors, and working models. However, machines have the disadvantage of limiting the amount of material that can be presented at a given time. Usually this limitation is imposed by the size of the display window in the machine. The materials designed for one teaching machine cannot be used with another machine. The typical science teacher does not have time to develop his own materials and must use what is available. If he is further constrained to use only those programs which can be accommodated by an available teaching machine, he is severely limited. Unfortunately, many of the producers of teaching machines have invested more of their time, talent, and money in the design and development of their equipment than they have in the programs to be used with these elaborate and costly devices.

Evaluation and Selection of Programed Materials

Overview of the Selection and Evaluation Process

Evaluation and selection is a dynamically interrelated five-step process, shown in Figure 10-5. Because this is a dynamic process, the steps need not be followed in the exact order given.

Usually the first step is to locate suitable programs by scanning bibliographies and catalogues. A program's initial suitability depends upon the relevance of its subject matter, the appropriateness of its reading level, the complexity of its content, and the amount of time required for its completion. Programs which do not meet these predetermined criteria are not considered.

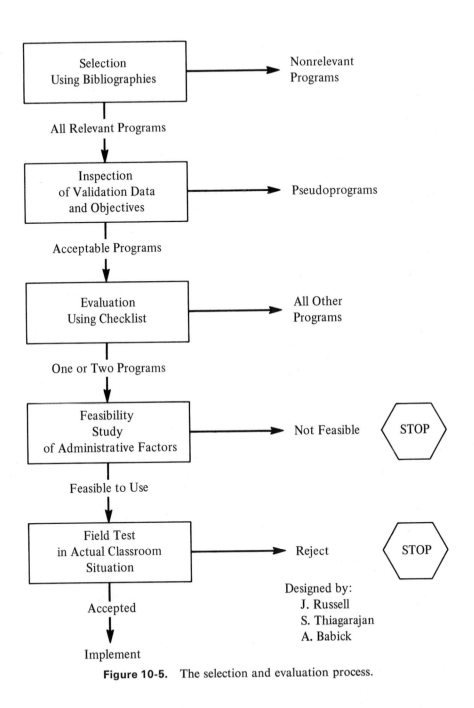

Figure 10-5. The selection and evaluation process.

When searching the literature for programs, the teacher should be suspicious of those programs which do not have stated objectives and validation data. Such materials could more appropriately be called pseudoprograms. They may include traditional textbooks disguised as programs which feature short statements to be read and blanks to be completed by the student.

After recognizing and eliminating the pseudoprograms, the teacher should make arrangements to examine those programs which seem to be compatible with his requirements. Publishers are usually willing to send a copy for examination; sometimes copies can be borrowed from a program library or an instructional materials center in a large city school system or university. A checklist such as Figure 10-5 can be used to estimate the educational potential of these programs.

Then such nonacademic factors as the following should be considered: "Do the programs require expensive teaching machines?" "Can the school afford to purchase enough copies to meet your needs?"

If it is feasible to use the programs, a field test should be conducted in an actual classroom or with a small group of students. For example, an earth science teacher is considering using one of two available programs to teach the geologic time scale. He could give each program to a separate class and evaluate the results as described later in this section.

Bibliographies of Programed Materials

In the selection of appropriate instructional materials for use in a science classroom, the teacher must consider his predetermined objectives regarding the subject matter to be taught (or what he wants the students to do), as well as the students' entry behavior (or how much the students know already). These characteristics of the instructional situation must be compared with the information provided by the publishers of commercially available programs.

There are currently two up-to-date bibliographies of programed materials, Entelek's *Programed Instruction Guide*, 2nd ed., 1968 (compiled by Northeastern University and published by Entelek, Incorporated; Newburyport, Massachusetts. Price $14) and Carl Hendershot's *Bibliography of Programs and Presentation Devices*, 4th ed., 1969 (compiled and published by Carl H. Hendershot; 4114 Ridgewood Drive; Bay City, Michigan. Price $27.50).

Entelek *Guide*

The Entelek *Guide* is compiled by electronic data-processing procedures, and the information provided is current, accurate, extensive in coverage, and capable of rapid revision. The *Guide* is published in book form from a computer data bank. Consequently, it is possible to update the *Guide* rapidly, integrate new information, and perform special data-manipulation tasks with a minimum of human effort. It consists of three sections: (1) the preface and relevant appendixes; (2) the index, which classifies available programs by subject matter; and (3) the data bank, which contains available information about the individual programs.

The data bank usually includes the following information for each program listed: title, author, producer, device requirement (if a teaching machine is needed), teacher's manual (whether or not a teacher's manual is available), tests available, assessment data, style (linear, branching, or hybrid), time needed to complete the program, level of the target population, cost, and publication date.

The *Guide*, in its second edition, lists over 2,220 programs in 186 subject-matter areas. The names and addresses of 445 sources of programs are also included. Programs listed range in completion time from less than one hour to several hundred hours and in cost from less than one dollar to several thousand dollars.

Hendershot *Bibliography*

Hendershot's *Bibliography of Programs and Presentation Devices* is now in its fourth edition. The loose-leaf notebook format allows for the addition of updating supplements. The bibliography is divided into four sections:

Section A. A listing of programs classified by subject. The subjects are listed alphabetically from "Adult Basic Education" to "Welding."

Section B. A listing of programs according to the publisher. The publishers are listed alphabetically, with all of their programs including the same information provided in Section A.

Section C. A listing of devices (teaching machines) which assist in the presentation of programs. Information is given about the manufacturers, and a brief description of each device is provided, including cost.

Section D. A reference to books and periodicals which pertain to programed instruction.

The information given in the *Guide* and *Bibliography* should enable the science teacher to determine if programs are available for use in his classroom.

However, reading about programs does not replace the need for examining them firsthand. Therefore, teachers should always request examination copies, any accompanying manuals, and particularly, the validation data for those programs that seem potentially useful.

The Key Question

When the science teacher is called upon to select programed materials for use in the classroom, there are many considerations to be made, but one *key* question to consider is, "What will the program teach to whom under what circumstances and in what length of time?" This complex question can be broken down into four separate questions:

1. *What does the program teach?* The answer to this question may be found in the list of *performance objectives,* assuming they are actually achieved by the program, or it may be found by comparing the *pretest and posttest results* of a number of students who have completed the program.

2. *Whom does the program teach?* The answer to this question is found in the description of the *target population.* The description should include the range of reading abilities, I.Q.'s, and previous achievement. If a program is designated for a certain age or grade level, it does not necessarily follow that everyone of that age or at that grade level will benefit from it.

3. *Under what circumstances does the program teach?* The answer to this question pertains to how the program should be administered. Does it require a teaching machine? If so, what model? Must the teacher be present? What are the scheduling requirements? Does the program require supplementary or adjunct materials?

4. *What length of time is necessary for the student to complete the program successfully?* The answer to this question includes the time *range,* as well as the *mean, median,* and *mode* times. This information is very important for scheduling considerations and for efficiency determinations. Perhaps the teacher or a traditional text could achieve the same objectives in less time and at a lower cost, and hence function more efficiently than the program.

Of course there are other factors that must be considered in the selection of programed materials. Specifically, how does the program fit into your curriculum? Included in this consideration are the *topics* covered by the program, the student *skills* and *knowledge* to be developed, and the *difficulty level* of the material. Reliable research information includes gains in student achievement and changes in student attitudes toward both the subject matter and the programed learning approach. This documented evidence should assist potential users in making decisions regarding a program's academic feasibility.

Another important consideration is the instructional situation in which the programed materials will be used. Will the program do the total teaching of the topic? Will it be used as remedial material? Enrichment material? Or perhaps to bring various students to the same entry level of understanding? Performance data should reveal a program's ability to serve these purposes.

Finally, and most importantly, can the school system afford the programed materials? In addition to the initial investment, the approach may require replacement of *expendable supplies*. If teaching machines are to be used, *maintenance costs* must be considered. What is the projected cost per student hour? How does this compare with the cost of other strategies?

Inspection

There are two main techniques used to evaluate programed materials, a checklist and field testing. A basic premise of programing is that each program's instructional effectiveness must be determined as a result of its demonstrated merits.

To evaluate programed materials adequately it is helpful to have

1. A copy of the program.
2. A statement regarding the prerequisite knowledge (entry behavior) of the intended population.
3. The specific teaching objectives of the program.
4. A description of how and with whom (target population) the program has been tested.
5. A statistical evaluation of the test results.

A program complete with the preceding information is very rarely available. Generally, only the program is available, thus making it the only basis for evaluation.

An inspection of a program with its objectives and validation data will indicate its probable effectiveness with your students.

Figure 10-6 contains a checklist for inspecting programed materials.

A Feasibility Study

A feasibility study should be conducted before any programed materials are adopted. The study should yield affirmative answers to the following questions:

1. Can acceptable patterns of scheduling group and individual class activities be achieved?
2. If equipment and other special facilities are involved, can acceptable arrangements be made for housing, scheduling, and maintenance?
3. Are costs in line with available funds? (Consideration must be given

YES NO

Objectives
    Is the program accompanied by a list of objectives stated in specific behavioral terms (i.e., student performance)?

Instructions
    Does the program have a self-contained set of instructions on how to use it?

Information
    Is an overview of the material provided?

    Is the information accurate and up-to-date?

    Is the reading level suitable for the intended population?

    Are technical terms and symbols adequately defined?

    Does the content cover the stated objectives, yet is the program "lean" (without superfluous and redundant material)?

    Do the frames contain only critical verbiage (i.e., information needed to respond to the questions)?

    Does the program periodically review what has been taught?

    Does the post-test measure the student's comprehension of the content of the program?

Questions
    Are the questions related to the objectives of the program?

    Do the questions have a wide variety of formats (fill-in, multiple-choice, matching, direct questions, drawing figures, etc.) to accomplish different purposes and to maintain student interest?

    Is the type of question used appropriate to the purpose of the frame (matched to actual performance conditions)?

    Do the questions require the learner to use all the critical (most important) information in the frame?

Figure 10-6.   Checklist for evaluating programed materials.

Do the questions require the learner to "understand" or apply the information presented in the frame rather than merely analyzing the cues and prompts or copying some words from the information?

Do the questions avoid asking the student to recall information presented in a previous frame but *not* "established" (i.e., not used by the student when responding to the question in the previous frame)?

Are enough questions used to allow the learner to apply the information to a variety of situations?

Confirmation

Are the confirmations presented in such a way that they are not easily exposed accidentally?

Are the confirmations accurate and clear to the student?

Is the student given freedom to deviate from the given confirmation by the indication that an equivalent response or a different order of items is acceptable?

Are helpful remedial comments provided when wrong or alternative answers are anticipated?

Do the instructions allow the learner to skip unnecessary repetition and to return to previous material when necessary?

Criterion Frames

Are the criterion frames readily recognizable and relevant to the stated objectives of the program?

Media

If media is used is it relevant to the program?

Does the program use media (visuals, audio-tape, or actual materials) when and where appropriate?

Validation Data

Is the program accompanied with validation data including:

a. target population (entry behavior)
b. instructional situation
c. time taken to complete program (median & range)
d. gain in student achievement
e. change in attitude
   i. toward subject matter
   ii. toward programed instruction?

Figure 10-6—*continued.*

to both initial and continuing costs for supplies, equipment, maintenance, supervision, and so on.)

4. Can acceptable patterns be arranged for coordinating the progress of classes using the program with that of other classes?

Field Testing

Potential users cannot always assess reliably the effectiveness of a program by merely inspecting it. Several studies have shown a high *negative* correlation between "effectiveness" ratings obtained from a panel of "experts" and the experimental evidence acquired in the field. In other words, those materials that the experts *thought* were superior programs were inferior when actually used with students.

Therefore to verify the consequences of using a program in a particular science classroom, the teacher should try out the material on a limited scale before large-scale adoption. The group of students used for field testing should include the ability range of those students who will use the program if it is adopted. Evidence for the effectiveness of a programed sequence should be based on a carefully conducted study which shows what the program's use accomplished under specific conditions. Such a study should use suitable measurements before (pretest) and after (posttest), with control procedures to ensure that gains can be attributed to the program and are not the result of other instruction. Field testing forces the program to speak for itself! How well does it teach what it is supposed to teach?

Detailed information on conducting such a field test of a program before using it on a large-scale basis can be found in an excellent little book entitled *A Guide to Evaluating Self-instructional Programs* by Jacobs, Maien, and Stolurow (published by Holt, Rinehart & Winston, 1966).

Utilization of Programed Materials

Uses of Programed Materials

By itself or in conjunction with other strategies a program can be used to teach part of a course or even an entire course. Many teachers are using short programed units to teach scientific principles and terminology. Programed instruction is particularly useful as enrichment instruction for students who are highly motivated to learn more about a subject. Learning can be continued and enhanced for these students even if the teacher does not have the time or ability to satisfy their inquiries. At the other end of the continuum, remedial instruction can also be accomplished by using programs. In the typical high school individual attention to "slow learners" is impossible because of class size. These students can use "tutorial" programs in lieu of a teacher's personal help. They can even take their "tutor" out of the classroom! Many teachers have reported "tremendous success" with programs in this area of instruction. Their positive results have been attributed to the fact that many below-average students are succeeding for the first time, and educational psychologists tell us that nothing enhances success better than success itself.

Programed instruction can also be used in the science classroom to achieve a certain prerequisite level of competence or "entry behavior." For example, as a high school physics teacher, the author used a self-developed program to teach his students power-of-10 notation, which is necessary to develop skill in solving physics problems. At the onset some of the students were more proficient with power-of-10 manipulations than their instructor; others had been introduced to the technique but lost competence because they were not required to use their newly acquired skill; still others had never been introduced to it. The instructional program on power-of-10 notation eliminated devoting class time to the subject which, because of student diversity, would have bored some and confused others. The students were able to master the material on their own. Those who knew the technique could ignore the program; those who had previously learned the skill but were a little "rusty" used the program as a review; and those who had never been exposed to power-of-10 notation learned the necessary manipulations on their own. All students were subsequently required to pass a criterion test demonstrating mastery of power-of-10 manipulations.

Programs can provide a continuous learning experience for students who miss specific instruction because they were absent. Programed instruction is especially useful for students who are hospitalized or confined at home. Assembling commercially prepared programs is also less expensive than hiring a private tutor for an extended period of time.

Programed Instruction in the Classroom

Before implementing a program into the curriculum it is imperative that the teacher carefully study the entire program. The teacher will then be able to provide more effective coordination with other instructional activities, such as lectures, group discussions, laboratory assignments, and films. It is important to remember that a steady diet of any instructional activity is less stimulating for the student than an approach that involves a variety of educational experiences.

The student's first exposure to programed materials is particularly important. Because attitudes toward new instructional strategies are usually formulated upon initial contact, students should experience immediate success with the materials. Teachers may deem it necessary to spend a few minutes explaining the programed approach to learning. The fact that a program is not a test should be emphasized. Traditional teaching practices cause many students to suffer from extreme test anxiety; consequently, when confronted with a series of questions, they become fearful of making errors. Because programs are for teaching and not for testing, the teacher should never evaluate students on the basis of their performance in the program. Rather, evaluation should be based upon the students' performance on criterion tests administered after using the program.

It should be established that each student will be working at his own pace, neither pushed faster than he can efficiently perform nor held back if he works rapidly. Students should be encouraged to ask questions at any time, and especially if the material seems confusing. Therefore it is important that the teacher be in the classroom and not in the teachers' lounge. The teacher can also spot weaknesses in the programs from these student comments.

The mechanics of using a programed textbook or tutorial laboratory should be explained briefly. Clarify whether answers are to be recorded in the textbook or on a separate sheet of paper. Recording the answers on a separate sheet allows the texts to be used again and again. Encourage students to be intellectually honest, inform them of the futility of just copying the correct answer from the confirmation booklet. Teachers report that although there is some initial peeking at the answers, such behavior disappears when students discover that they can understand the material better and can get the correct answer without looking ahead.

The proper use of programed instruction in the science classroom changes the role of the teacher from a *disseminator of knowledge* to a *director of learning*. Many present-day science teachers are practitioners of the "show-and-tell" method of presenting information. These teachers mistakenly assume that presentation of information is automatically followed by learning. Rather, the teacher becomes an arranger of conditions necessary for the students to achieve the desired learning objectives, instead of a relater of information to be recorded, remembered, and regurgitated.

Programed instruction will not replace the teacher. The teacher should be on hand to direct the students' activities with imagination and understanding. Instructional programs can handle the drill and review, thus freeing the teacher from the drudgery of repetitive activities and providing time for work with small groups or individual students.

When relieved of time-consuming explanations and routine presentations, the science teacher has time to prepare for individual needs and to inspire further achievement through dynamic and creative education. The teacher becomes a diagnostician. He should be able to detect a loss of interest or careless errors on the part of the students. The teacher should establish the following: Does each student have adequate prerequisite information? Does each student display evidence of comprehension? Does the student already have the desired terminal behavior?

The teacher may be a prescriber of instruction, attempting to outline a program of study which will meet the needs of each individual student. The goal should be for each student to *master* a maximum amount of material instead of for the class to cover a required amount of text material for course credit.

Whether using programed materials or not, an important function of the teacher should be to create and maintain interest. This may be accomplished by staging mind-capturing demonstrations. Some teachers prefer to arouse interest with a preliminary discussion; others recommend showing a film which imparts a general overview of the subject area. Serving as a tutor for those students who have minor difficulties with the materials and answering questions not discussed in the program, the teacher becomes a resource person for the entire class.

Even though a program may provide instruction in the absence of a teacher, several research studies have shown that a teacher-plus-program combination was superior to either a teacher or a program alone. Therefore, each should be used to perform the tasks for which it is best suited. However, the single most important factor influencing the success of programed materials in the classroom is the *teacher*.

Using Modular Units or Minicourses

One effective use of programed materials is to divide a course into a number of specific units. Such modular units may be completed within a few hours, and some of them are available from commercial publishers. The short units can be integrated with other science classroom activities, such as laboratories, lectures, and field trips. These modular units or minicourses are self-contained instructional packages dealing with a single conceptual unit of subject matter. They are another attempt to individualize learning by enabling each student to proceed independently through the material. The multifaceted learning experiences are for the most part presented in a self-instructional format. The student controls the rate and intensity of his study. Because minicourses usually involve materials that are portable, the student can take them to the library, to a study carrel, or to his home. Minicourses are typically designed for use by one or two students, but they can be used by a larger group. Their lengths vary from fifteen minutes of student time to several hours. The minicourses can be used independently or combined in a variety of different sequences.

Minicourses utilize a wide variety of instructional activities: conducting experiments, examining diagrams and photographs, viewing films and colored slides, handling real objects and models, studying demonstration materials, and listening to tape recordings. All sensory inputs should be made available to the student in mastering the objectives of the minicourse. Each student can use any or all of the media and materials available. The selection of the most appropriate approach is often left to the student. As with other programed instruction, the student assumes greater responsibility for his own learning.

Computerized Instruction in Science Education

Introduction to Computerized Instruction

The computer, with its almost instantaneous response to student input, its extensive capacity to store and manipulate information, and its un-matched ability to serve many individuals simultaneously, offers great promise for science instruction. Because computers have large capacities for storing information pertaining to students, including past performance and individual needs, course content, and alternate learning sequences, it becomes possible to retrieve and use this information whenever it is needed to optimize instruction. The computer has the ability to manage and control a wide variety of learning materials—films, filmstrips, random access slides, audio tapes, and printed texts—which can be available at the appropriate time. The computer can also record, analyze, and react to student responses that are typed from a typewriter keyboard or indicated with a "light pen" on a cathode ray screen. Consequently, the computer is a dynamic instructional tool which extends the application and implementation of programed instruction by providing for additional flexibility and greater individualization.

In science education the computer can perform many roles and add new dimensions to learning. The most obvious applications are solving numerical problems and analyzing data generated in laboratory exercises. The computer can also be utilized for drill and practice, tutorial assistance, inquiry training, simulation of laboratory exercises, and dialogue with the student. Drill and practice activities present principles and rules that are repeated until the student demonstrates comprehension. In the tutorial role, programed materials which require application and analysis of scientific principles are presented by the computer. Therefore this technique can be used to develop concepts. Dialogue with the computer allows the student to ask questions rather than merely to give answers. The computer presents a problem and provides a framework in which the student can proceed to a solution. The alternative progression patterns of the material are numerous and flexible, thus providing for nearly complete individualization.

There are basically two types of systems for computerized instruction, Computer Assisted Instruction (CAI) and Computer Managed Instruction (CMI). In CAI the student interacts directly with the computer, which stores the instructional material and sequential logic. Branching techniques are facilitated by the computer. The student who answers incorrectly is directed to a remedial branch which explains the material in more detail. The computer is a patient teacher which repeats explanations and gives examples until the student demonstrates mastery. The second type of system, Computer Managed Instruction (CMI), uses the computer to help teachers administer and guide the instructional process, but it relies on separate equipment and learning materials for instruction. The student is not "on line," or directly connected with the computer system, and instructional material itself is not stored in the computer. However, the computer does store student information and lists of instructional materials that can be retrieved rapidly. It solves many logistical problems. In addition, the computer can diagnose the learning needs of an entire class and can prescribe the optimal sequence of instruction.

Computer Hardware and Programs

A simple computer-based learning station has a teletypewriter connected to a central computer, either directly or by telephone lines. The computer need not be in the vicinity of the student station. In fact, it may be in another part of the school, in another town, or even in another part of the country. At the learning station instructional information is typed by the computer. References to visual materials, equipment, and models are given when necessary. The student responds by typing his answer on the teletype terminal. The computer then compares his answer with a series of stored responses and informs him of his correctness, and subsequently presents the student with or directs the student to additional stimulus material.

In more complicated systems visual materials are presented on a cathode ray tube or flashed from a computer-controlled slide projector onto a screen.

With the cathode ray tube the student may use a "light pen" to indicate the correct response directly on the screen. The use of the light pen to draw figures on the cathode ray tube provides dimensions for the teaching of mathematical and scientific concepts. The computer can also be programed to recognize typed words. Because effective learning takes place through sound, such audio equipment as a loudspeaker or head set is sometimes installed in student stations. Prerecorded tapes can then be used as part of the instructional sequence.

Typical of the several approaches to using CAI for teaching chemistry is IBM's simulated version of one section of a qualitative analysis laboratory. The student is asked to identify individual metals in a group using a sequence of tests on a hypothetical sample containing all of the metals. The student instructs the computer "to perform a certain analysis." A code system representing drops, molarity, and reagents is employed by the student, and he indicates whether such techniques as filtration and centrifugation are to be used. The computer responds with the appropriate colored picture resulting from the student's procedures and with a typed verification when the student succeeds in identifying a particular metal in the sample.

Currently there are two relevant bibliographies of computer-assisted instruction programs. The *Computer-Assisted Instruction Guide* is compiled and published by Entelek, Incorporated; 42 Pleasant Street; Newburyport, Massachusetts 01950. The *Index to Computer Assisted Instruction* is compiled and published by the Instructional Media Laboratory at the University of Wisconsin at Milwaukee.

Advantages and Disadvantages of Computerized Instruction

A technique called time sharing permits as many as 200 students to use the same computer at the same time. Consequently, smaller school systems with limited budgets can share computer facilities with other schools.

In addition to the actual instructional materials, the computer also stores information pertaining to each student, including his age, aptitude scores, personality traits, previous responses, and speed of responding. Thus when a student types his name and identification number on the teletype, the student's records can be assessed and the computer can without delay present review material, or it can resume exactly where the student stopped previously. The student's accurate and complete records stored in the computer can also be made available to teachers for an evaluation of his progress.

At present the cost of one hour of student time on a CAI system may be as high as several hundred dollars. The initial cost of the hardware is also high. As with programed instruction, designing and developing CAI materials is very expensive and time-consuming. Not only must each lesson be designed, developed, and validated, but the entire sequence must be put into computer language. Learning the computer language may be an obstacle to potential developers of CAI materials. The total process from analyzing the task to having the material tested and available on a computer terminal may involve more than 100 man-hours per hour of student time. There are also problems regarding the range of answers which the computer will accept from the student. Consequently, there are relatively few CAI programs on the market, and many of these are applicable to only one particular computer system, which eliminates interchanging from one computer to another.

At present, technological, economic, and educational problems plague the use and development of CAI systems. One key technological problem is "down time" (when the system is inoperable because of a malfunction). For the student who is eager to learn, it is very disheartening to have the machine break down in the middle of a learning sequence. However, the only solution is to wait patiently until the system can be repaired.

Computerized instruction, despite its many disadvantages today, has the potential for dynamic science teaching in the not too distant future. Contemporary teachers must be aware of the computer's potential, even though few school systems have incorporated this strategy into their instruction. From programed instruction the computer is the next logical step toward *completely* individualized instruction.

Additional References

Edling, Jack V., et al. *Four Case Studies in Programed Instruction.* New York: Fund for the Advancement of Education, 1964.

Mager, Robert F. *Preparing Instructional Objectives.* Palo Alto, Calif.: Fearon Publishers, 1962.

National Society for the Study of Education. *Programed Instruction Sixty-sixth Yearbook.* Chicago: University of Chicago Press, 1967.

Pipe, Peter. *Practical Programing.* New York: Holt, Rinehart & Winston, Inc., 1966.

Silverman, Robert E. *How to Use Programed Instruction in the Classroom.* Cambridge, Mass.: Honor Products Company, 1967.

reading skill development

Science teachers frequently dismiss their responsibility for improving the reading skills of their students with simple comments like, "I have too much science to teach," or "I don't have enough time to teach reading." Some science teachers adopt nontextbook approaches, to avoid frustrating students with textbooks they cannot read. However, most science teachers want their students to continue reading about science in books, scientific journals, news magazines, and/or newspapers throughout their lives. The science teacher who is interested in immediate student achievement as well as the long-range goal of continuous science reading must emphasize reading in his science teaching.

High schools generally give considerable attention to developing reading programs for remedial readers. This does not mean that science teachers can defer all responsibility for the improvement of reading skills of remedial readers, or other students, to the reading specialists. Reading teachers often concentrate their effort on the development of basic skills useful for a wide range of materials and purposes. They are generally not concerned with the particular content being used, but will select passages which will provide the student with practice on the skills being emphasized. The science teacher, on the other hand, should be concerned with both the content and the skills required of the student to achieve mastery of the content. He should give direct attention to those reading skills needed to understand the selections he assigns. The science teacher should not attempt to focus on reading skills, as does the reading teacher, nor should he provide isolated practice on specific reading skills that are not related to the unit of study under consideration. The science teacher should simply help his students successfully read the specific assignments that he gives.

Every science teacher realizes that many students have problems reading assigned materials. Few teachers realize the extent or nature of the problems faced by students. For example, did you know that

1. College honor roll candidates have inefficient study techniques and typically do not read at a rate significantly better than average college students.
2. If a student is given a quiz over a reading he just completed, he will only answer 60 per cent of the answers correctly; if he rereads the material immediately, his comprehension will only increase 5 per cent.
3. Two weeks after reading a given assignment, a student will forget all but 20 per cent of the assignment.
4. When students are given instruction in reading and study skills along with studies of the content area (e.g., science), significant improvement of the student's ability to learn and remember the content material is evidenced.[1]

What Are Some of the Reading Problems Faced by Science Students?

In this chapter the reading problems faced by science students are arbitrarily classified as problems caused directly by the teacher and inherent science reading problems over which the teacher has a lesser degree of control. Both sets of problems are "real" and must be dealt with specifically.

Common Teacher-Caused Problems

Teachers intensify reading problems by (1) assigning the same reading to all students, (2) failing to ascertain the functional vocabulary level of

[1] F. P. Robinson, "Study Skills for Superior Students in Secondary School," *Reading Teacher*, Vol. 15 (September, 1961), pp. 29–33, 37.

the student and beginning instruction at that level, and (3) failing to deal directly with the specific factors which make the reading of science materials difficult.

Science teachers assign reading of a wide variety of materials. Although this common practice of many science teachers could positively affect the development of reading skills in their students, the opposite is usually true. Because the quality of writing and readability of these materials varies extensively, care must be taken to get the best materials to each student. The habit of assigning a wide variety of reading materials must be linked to a practice of assigning the more readable materials to those students with fewer reading skills. For example, better readers may be assigned to read an article from *Scientific American*, whereas average and poor readers may be assigned to read a selection on the same topic in *Science World*.

Concepts and corresponding vocabulary are usually introduced on an ascending scale of difficulty. The reader is required to use his previous knowledge and experience to interpret the new concepts presented. If the teacher does not evaluate the quantity and quality of the student's previous experience and knowledge and does not begin instruction at the appropriate level, he may discover that the textbook and his instruction are beyond the functioning level of his students. Science words are typically more specific and more descriptive than words in other disciplines. They often have new specific science definitions as well as semantic variations in other contexts with which the student is already familiar. Moreover, science words are frequently composed of prefixes, suffixes, and stems which may add to the confusion of learning the vocabulary if students are not taught to examine words for these elements. Knowledge of a single stem, prefix, or suffix may lead to the understanding of hundreds of words. In addition to developing student skill in examining word components, the teacher should relate all words to the classifications, processes, or concepts they describe. In many cases it is advisable to develop an understanding of the concept, process, or classification prior to introducing the formal vocabulary.

Students who may be classified as relatively good readers by teachers in other content areas, or by their scores on general reading tests, often have problems reading science materials. To become a successful science reader, the student needs direct training in the particular skills that are consistently needed in science reading and that are not generally developed in other areas or through general reading. Because many of these types of reading problems appear to be inherent, teachers have little direct control over them. However, because they are inherent to science reading, teachers should deal with them specifically and directly.

Inherent Science Reading Problems

Science reading materials are terse, have a large specific vocabulary, and require the extensive use of critical reading skills.

The rate of introduction of ideas and concepts of science generally proceeds much faster than in other reading materials. Thus *terse* is the best single word description of science reading materials. The terse style of science readings, although much valued, does not contribute to making science reading easy. It is particularly difficult reading for students who have not learned to vary their reading rate to match the material. Science material must usually be read slowly and deliberately. Because students have been trained to read at rates much faster than the rate required by science materials, they must be encouraged to slow down and read more deliberately.

The large, specific vocabulary has been referred to earlier, but because teachers do not control writers, it is mentioned again. Efforts to control the vocabulary level of textbooks have not met with much success. There is not only a wide variation between different texts, but within a single text. It is not uncommon to discover a chapter containing college-level vocabulary in a junior high school textbook. The vocabulary problem emphasizes the need for classroom sets of a large number of books with various levels of readability, which would permit the teacher to make differential reading assignments.

Although the terse style and extensive vocabulary makes science reading difficult, the general lack of critical reading skills is probably the most important single inhibitor of successful science reading. The critical reading skill required for successful science reading is generally not emphasized in reading programs. Elementary reading programs focus their attention on developing the literal reading skills.

Literal reading is the ability to interpret information that is explicitly stated. Although the ability to read literally is a necessary entry skill for science reading, to become a good science reader the student must also develop critical reading skills which involve a level of interpretation higher than that needed for literal reading. Maney describes fourteen skills needed to become a good, critical reader.[2] As you read the definition of these skills, begin to think how you might discover whether your students are prepared to be critical readers and what you might do if they are not.

1. *Functional vocabulary:* Does the student have an experiential background with the vocabulary?

[2] Ethel S. Maney, "Literal and Critical Reading in Science," *Journal of Experimental Education*, Vol. 27 (September, 1958).

2. *Semantic variation of vocabulary:* Can the student identify similar uses of the same word?
3. *Central theme:* Can the student distinguish the central topic of a selection from subordinate topics?
4. *Key idea:* Can the student identify the key or most important idea in the story?
5. *Inference:* Is the student able to draw specific conclusions from facts explicitly stated?
6. *Generalization:* Is the student able to separate a general conclusion, or principle, from information implicitly stated?
7. *Problem solving:* Can the student apply information given him in a written communication toward solving a problem?
8. *Association of ideas:* Can the student describe the relationship among a series of ideas presented him in a written communication?
9. *Analogy:* Can the student perceive the relationship between two pairs of ideas?
10. *Antecedent:* Is the student able to recognize the word, or words, to which a pronoun refers?
11. *Sequence:* Is the student able to determine a time sequence?
12. *Extraneous ideas:* Is the student able to separate relevant from extraneous ideas presented in a written communication?
13. *Following directions:* Can the student follow directions?
14. *Visualization:* Is the student able to interpret a graphic representation and translate the ideas to a verbal form?

Simply knowing the range and extent of the reading problems of students is only interesting commentary. If, however, you could discover the range and extent of specific reading problems of your own students, the interesting commentary would be transformed into a realistic and relevant commentary on problems you and your students should work to solve.

How Can Reading Problems Be Diagnosed?

This portion of the chapter will describe some informal reading tests that can be designed and used by teachers. Using these tests will not qualify you as a specialist in reading and reading problems. They will simply help you discover the major competencies and incompetencies of your students. You may ask the school's reading specialist to assist you in constructing these tests or in examining them to determine if an important dimension has been omitted or overlooked. The reading specialist may also assist you in designing practice exercises which will help your students gain effective study skills and become better science readers and thereby better science students. Science teachers are not expected to develop expertise in diagnosing reading problems or prescribing reading instruction. The school's reading specialist should be so trained and typically will want to assist you in your attempts to improve your student's science reading ability.

Informal reading tests can be constructed to determine (1) if the students can read the basic text, (2) what level of reading material is appropriate if the text is too difficult, and (3) if the students are critical readers.

Is the Basic Text Appropriate?

A textbook is appropriate if students can find information in it, read the information, and relate this information to other topics and problems which require this information for solution.

Finding Information

A simple means of discovering if the student can find material in the book is to ask him to locate answers to factual questions in the book. Tests may be used to discover if students can use the table of contents, index, appendixes, major headings, and minor headings in their search for information. A few examples of this type of informal test follow. These sample items may be used to discover whether students can find information in the ESCP book *Investigating the Earth*.[3]

List the page number(s) on which the following information can be found.

Page(s)
_____ 1. A definition of *isobar*.
_____ 2. A comparison of the Fahrenheit, Celcius, and Kelvin scales.
_____ 3. A discussion of the solar system.
_____ 4. The table of contents.
_____ 5. Appendix E, Part I.
_____ 6. The index page which refers to discontinuity.
_____ 7. A definition of *half-life*.

[3] Earth Science Curriculum Project, *Investigating the Earth* (Boston: Houghton Mifflin Company, 1967), 594 pp.

These seven items are only examples. To determine reliably whether or not your students can find information in the text, you should probably construct at least twenty items. The number of correctly answered items and the time a student takes to complete the items indicates his ability to use the text as an information source. Many, and perhaps most, of your students will be very proficient in using the text and should be routed into another activity immediately. Those students who exhibit little proficiency should receive instruction on textbook utilization immediately.

The simplest way to discover if your students can read the text is to have them read a selection to you out loud. Reading out loud is generally not a good testing method in secondary classes because you create a situation in which good readers must listen to poor readers stumble through a paragraph and poor readers are frequently exposed to inappropriate sounds which imitate or make fun of their feeble efforts. But if small groups of individuals can be isolated, an oral reading test will often provide a wealth of information concerning a student's reading ability.

Paper-and-pencil tests are generally more appropriate because all students can be involved simultaneously. The first test described could easily be used as an oral or a paper-and-pencil test.

Test 1 (Open Book)

1. Direct the students to read a paragraph in their book and with their book open summarize the paragraph in their own words. (You may also have the students interpret and explain graphs, describe and summarize information given in charts, and discuss the significance of a photograph or picture.)
2. Direct the students to another selection. (Paragraph, graph, chart, photograph, or picture.) Ask them to relate the information contained in the selection to something else, such as another area of study, their personal lives, hobbies, or other interests.
3. Select several words and direct the students to define the words in their own terms. Defined words should fit the context of the selection.
4. Discuss answers to all parts. (Students could either correct their own papers or exchange papers.)

Test 2 (Closed Book)

1. Direct the students to read a selection in the book. When they have read the selection, ask them to write down the time indicated on the board. (You can write the time on the board in 10-second intervals.)

2. Direct the student to answer questions on the selection without looking back at it.
3. Discuss the answers to all questions.

Teachers frequently discover that many of their students cannot read the basic text. What the student can read should then become the paramount concern.

What Can My Students Read?

An informal test to discover what your students can read will generally provide you with more pertinent information than a general reading test because you will discover the student's skill in a science context. An informal reading-level test can be constructed by writing several paragraphs of increasing difficulty and following each paragraph with questions. The students should answer the questions without looking back at the paragraph. The number of paragraphs and questions successfully answered by your students will indicate the appropriate level of science reading materials.

Another and perhaps better means of informally determining the appropriate level of reading materials is to select paragraphs on the same topic from various available sources. (Elementary and junior high school texts, or textbooks, especially written for students with reading problems.) Once you discover which source is best for a particular student, you may have him study from that source rather than the basic text. You must, however, remember that there may be a wide variation in reading level from chapter to chapter, or even from page to page, within a single source. Hence you must review continually the progress of your students on reading assignments. Perhaps you will be able to train your students to recognize when they do not understand a reading assignment and to communicate that fact to you.

What About Critical Reading?

Critical reading is a prime requisite for successful science reading. Informal reading tests of the student's critical reading ability can be contained within every quiz and test you administer. Examine the list of fourteen reading skills needed for critical reading which were described by Maney and cited on pp. 166 of this chapter. Compare these fourteen skills with the definitions of comprehension and analysis provided in Chapter 8.[4] The list of skills needed for critical reading and the cognitive activities of comprehension and analysis are very similar. You may use the comprehension and analysis items you construct for quizzes and examinations as informal critical reading tests.

Developing Your Student's Reading Skills

Describing and diagnosing reading problems is just an interesting intellectual game until the teacher uses the information discovered to select and design reading materials for his students. A science teacher can, with little effort, develop a purpose for reading the assignment, help students develop a functional vocabulary, make differential reading assignments, and help the student develop an efficient study technique. The teacher who, in his teaching, emphasizes these four skills will cause a greater degree of change (achievement), and this change will have a greater effect on the student's future progress and achievement.

Purpose

Students who have a specific reason for reading an assignment learn more from the assignment than students who read the assignment simply because they are "nice guys" who follow a teacher's directions. Teachers can develop an interest in reading assignments by relating reading assignments to things which occur outside the science classroom. For example, the question, "Why are you 'out of breath' after a race or exercise?" may interest a student in reading a few pages on respiration. Initially the teacher may provide questions for the student to answer after reading an assignment. These questions *must* be structured with care. If only knowledge questions are asked, the students will develop efficient search and copy techniques. However, most of the knowledge they copy will be forgotten shortly after they close the book. Postreading questions should at least force the student to translate, interpret, or extrapolate. Criteria for constructing postreading questions can be drawn from the discussion of Bloom's *Taxonomy*[5] or from Maney's list of critical reading skills.

[4] See Chapter 8, "Evaluating Specific Performances," or see Bloom's *Taxonomy of Educational Objectives*, Handbook I, *Cognitive Domain* (New York: David McKay, 1956).
[5] See Chapter 8, Evaluating Specific Performances, p. 94.

Eventually students should have the responsibility for constructing questions they hope to have answered through reading the assignment. In fact, because the major purpose for reading a science assignment should be answering a question, or series of questions, the teacher's initial emphasis should be placed on developing the student's ability to ask questions that can be answered by the reading assignment.

Vocabulary

Words are handy, economical tools which symbolize processes, classifications, and concepts. Like any tool, a word's function must be known before it can be used properly. Because science words frequently have very specific definitions, they may be compared to very precise tools, and their proper use should be given emphasis at least equal to that given the use of a microscope, oscilloscope, or expensive power source.

Teachers can assist students in developing a functional science vocabulary by teaching them to examine words and by consistently relating words to the processes, classifications, and concepts to which they refer. Taking the small amount of time needed to examine the prefixes, stems, and suffixes of a word makes many difficult words easy to understand and use. For example, the word *osmoregulation* is often difficult for beginning biology students until it is broken into *osmosis* and *regulation*. A few similarly difficult words which become relatively easy when broken into prefixes, suffixes, and stems include *anticline, epicenter, evapotranspiration, thermoresister, thermocline, regeneration,* and *infrared.* What are some other words which may present similar problems to students?

Differential Reading

Preparing differential reading assignments may be rather time-consuming initially, particularly if your classroom is not equipped with a wide range of reading material. A science room is not well equipped unless it has a large selection of science reading materials with a wide range of readability.

The idea of giving some students alternate reading assignments is not accepted by many teachers because they believe that if all students do not read the same assignment, they will not have the same equal opportunity to succeed in a testing situation. Although every student does not have the same opportunity to succeed in a testing situation, it cannot be concluded that his lack of success is related to a teacher's practice of making differential reading assignments. If a student cannot read the text, giving him the same textbook assignment as other students places him at a disadvantage. Giving him an assignment he *can* read, even if it contains only one-half as much information, is unquestionably a better practice.

Reading Study Techniques

Even the best readers are generally inefficient readers. Systematic reading study techniques, such as the SQ3R method, are designed to help students become more efficient readers.

What Is the SQ3R Method?

The SQ3R technique[6] was originally devised, from research findings, for use in studying college textbooks. Since its original application, it has been used with a wide variety of secondary school students. Reports citing the effectiveness of this technique have been optimistic. Students who use the technique (1) get more ideas from reading, (2) remember the ideas much better and longer, and (3) take better notes. Skill in learning the technique *cannot* be obtained by simply reading about it. Reading skill, like most skills, can be developed through practice. The five steps of the SQ3R method are

1. Survey. Skim over headings and summary to get a general idea of the content.
2. Ask a question before reading a section. Use section headings as a guide. Turn section headings into questions.
3. Read the section to answer the question.
4. Stop, recite. From memory write down the question and answer the question in phrases. This step forces the student to organize his answer. Using only phrases reduces writing time and generally provides enough cue for later study.
5. Review the lesson. Recite various points to fix them in mind.

Simply reading about this technique will not help the teacher, nor will merely telling or explaining this technique to students help them. To be of value, the technique must be practiced under supervision until mastered. Remember, becoming a better reader prepares the student to become a better science student.

[6] F. P. Robinson, *Effective Study*, revised ed. (New York: Harper & Row, 1961).

In addition to improving a science student's general reading study skills, science teachers who require special projects or research papers should emphasize the development of reference study skills. Reference study skills of particular importance in science include locating materials, evaluating materials, and organizing them into meaningful reports. The librarian will usually be very willing to assist you in this endeavor and may even be willing to teach your students how to find science materials in the library. You may even discover that it is possible to work out a joint assignment with the student's English teacher, who will focus attention on organizing the findings. The job of teaching students how to evaluate their findings should be the science teacher's special contribution.

Science Teaching and the Seriously Retarded Reader

All of the practices discussed in this chapter can be used with the seriously retarded reader. The need for these practices will be more evident and the effect of their utilization may be quite dramatic. If anything, you will discover that these practices are not enough, you may need to emphasize reading more extensively and use a greater variety of techniques. The authors urge you to seek out the assistance of a reading specialist, and if your school does not have one, argue and campaign for the establishment of such a position in your school.

Discussion Questions

1. To what extent should a science teacher also be a reading teacher?
2. You have been assigned the task of teaching general science to a population of eighth-graders whose educational backgrounds vary so extensively that the description *heterogeneous group* appears to be a euphemism. The resources at your command are many and varied. How will you proceed?
3. If you were assigned the task of teaching seventh-grade science to a group of students classified as nonreaders, how would you proceed?
4. Describe a science reading-skill development program you would be willing to implement in any school.

Additional References

Aaron, I. E. "Reading in Mathematics," *Journal of Reading*, Vol. 8 (May, 1965), pp. 391–95, 401.

Bamman, Henry A. "Reading in Science and Mathematics," *Perspectives in Reading Instruction in Secondary Schools*, Vol. 2 (1964). International Reading Association.

Buehler, Rose Burgess. "Innovations in High School Reading Instruction," *Proceedings*, Vol. 11 (1966), pp. 169–71.

Durr, William K. "Improving Secondary Reading Through the Content Subject," *Proceedings*, Vol. 8 (1963), pp. 66–69.

Gilder, Lister L. "Meeting Reading Demands of the Content Subjects," *Proceedings*, Vol. 11, Part I (1966), pp. 39–42.

Herber, Harold L. "Developing Reading Skills Demanded by Content Subjects," *Proceedings*, Vol. 11, Part I (1966), pp. 68–71.

Horsman, Gwen. "Some Useful Classroom Practices and Procedures in Reading in the Content Fields," *Proceedings*, Vol. 9 (1964), pp. 44–45.

Ladd, Eleanor M. "Individualizing Instruction in Classroom Corrective Situations," *Proceedings*, Vol. 11, Part I (1966), pp. 254–56.

Mallinson, George G. "Science Learning and the Problem Reader," *Perspectives in Reading*, 6, *Corrective Reading in the High School Classroom*, International Reading Association, 1966.

Maney, Ethel S. "Literal and Critical Reading in Science," *Journal of Experimental Education*, Vol. 27 (September, 1958).

Robinson, F. P. *Effective Study*, rev. ed. New York: Harper & Row, 1961.

Robinson, F. P. "Study Skills for Superior Students in Secondary School," *Reading Teacher*, Vol. 15 (September, 1961), pp. 29–33, 37.

Robinson, H. Alan. "Teaching Reading in the Content Areas: Some Basic Principles of Instruction," *Proceedings*, Vol. 9 (1964), pp. 35–36.

Shepherd, David L. "Teaching Science and Mathematics to the Seriously Retarded Reader in the High School," *Reading Teacher*, Vol. 17 (September, 1963), pp. 25–30.

Smith, Helen K. "Identification of Factors that Inhibit Progress in Reading," *Proceedings*, Vol. 10 (1965), pp. 200–202.

Spache, George D. "Types and Purposes of Reading in Various Curriculum Fields," *Reading Teacher*, Vol. 11 (February, 1958), pp. 158–64.

Vick, Nancy O'Neil. "High School Reading for the Severely Retarded," *Proceedings*, Vol. 11, Part I (1966), pp. 227–30.

Weiss, I. E. "Reading in Mathematics," *Journal of Reading*, Vol. 8 (May, 1965), pp. 391–95, 401.

Weiss, M. Jerry. *Reading in the Secondary Schools*. New York: The Odyssey Press, 1961:
Carter, Homer L. J. "Helping Students Read Scientific Material," pp. 341–45.
Eakin, Mary K. "Reading Skills and Habits Needed in Science," pp. 250–59.
"Science," pp. 346–50.
Strang, Ruth. "Teaching Reading in Science Classes," pp. 335–40.

testing, statistics, and a rationale for grading

This chapter provides a brief discussion of test construction, some useful statistics, and a few ideas on the assignment of grades. In Chapter 5 we described performance objectives and in Chapter 7 the evaluation of specific performances. The reader is encouraged to study the excellent sources cited in the footnotes.

Test-Item Construction

Most of the desired terminal performances should be identified and defined in measurable terms before the unit or block of subject matter is taught. The early definition of desired terminal performance is essential whenever the teacher wishes to draw inferences about his teaching effectiveness from student scores on an achievement test. If a teacher prepares all objectives and test items after the unit has been taught, his sample will be biased by his limited memory and by a host of other factors which probably cannot be defined.

The decision concerning test specifications should also occur before teaching begins. Instruction should be designed to encompass the full range of intellectual activity, and achievement tests should be a representative sample of the instruction. (See Chapter 7.) A representative sample can be obtained by randomly selecting a predetermined number of performances from the full list of performances. If, for example, you had 150 performance objectives for a given block of material, you could select randomly fifty objectives to use as the guidelines for test-item construction.

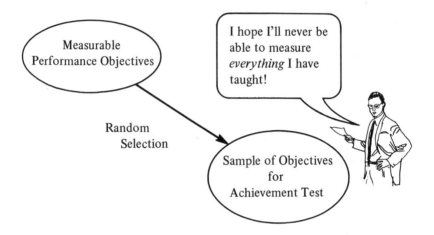

Test items can be designed at any time, and once a good test item is developed, it should be kept. Over the years a teacher should be able to develop a large collection of good test items. Beginning teachers should ask colleagues whether they have collections of items and should arrange to trade good items. The actual design of the item should be determined by the type of intellectual activity you are attempting to measure. It is probably impossible to measure a student's ability to synthesize or evaluate with true–false items; an essay item would be more appropriate. However, most test items should be of the multiple-choice variety for at least two reasons. First, students can complete many of them in a given time (a larger sample is generally more valid and reliable). Second, multiple-choice items can be designed to measure the first four levels of thought described by Bloom (knowledge, comprehension, application, analysis). No other type of test item satisfies the first reason and permits this wide range of measurement. Neither of these reasons, taken singly, is a strong argument for constructing multiple-choice examinations. However, because both considerations are essential, the multiple-choice item has become the favorite of test constructionists. Guidelines for the construction of this type of test item will be discussed first.

Multiple-Choice Test Items[1]

Multiple-choice items consist of a problem statement and a series of possible responses. The problem statement (stem) may be a question or an incomplete statement. Responses may consist of a correct answer and several plausible wrong answers or of several partially correct answers and one best answer. It is generally better to direct the student to select the best answer regardless of the type of responses given. Some rules to follow when constructing multiple-choice items include the following:

1. Avoid trivia. Each item should measure a stated, desired terminal performance.
2. State a single problem in the stem of the question.
3. Use simple, clear language.
4. Place most of the words in the stem of the question. Keep the responses as short as possible.
5. State the problem in positive form. Whenever a negative form is used, emphasize it in some way ("which of the following is not"— underline *not* for emphasis).
6. Be sure that the intended answer is clearly correct or definitely the best response.
7. Avoid giving clues such as
   a. Grammatically inconsistent responses.
   b. Similarity of wording between stem and a single response.
   c. Textbook language or stereotyped phraseology.
   d. Statement of the correct answers in greater detail.
   e. Inclusion of absolute terms.
   f. Inclusion of two responses with the same meaning.
8. Make the responses plausible and attractive to the uninformed.
9. Vary the length of correct responses.
10. Avoid using "all of the above" or "none of the above" as responses.
11. Randomize the position of the correct responses.
12. Be sure that each item on the test is independent of other items.

Matching Items[2]

Matching items are modifications of multiple-choice items which list a series of stems in one column and a series of plausible responses in another

[1] After Norman E. Gronlund, *Measurement and Evaluation in Teaching* (New York: Macmillan, 1967), pp. 140–59.
[2] Ibid.

column. The only time this type of item is appropriate is when all the responses are plausible answers to the problem statement of the stem. When all the responses are plausible, the matching item is simply a more efficient multiple-choice format. Rules for the construction of this type of item include the following:

1. The material of the item should be homogeneous. For example, the stems may be scientific achievements and the responses may be the names of scientists.
2. Use a larger or smaller number of responses than stems and indicate to students that responses may be used more than once.
3. Select only responses that are plausible.

True–False Items[3]

The true–false item is a statement which the student must judge true or false. Modifications of the basic pattern may require the student to respond *yes* or *no, fact* or *opinion, right* or *wrong*, or may direct him to correct the false statements by altering the terminology. True–false items should be avoided because it is extremely difficult to construct items that measure significant terminal performances while maintaining the unqualifiedly true or unqualifiedly false criteria requirement. Qualifying the statements to make them absolutely true or false usually provides clues to the student. Other reasons for avoiding true–false items include the fact that an uninformed student has a fifty-fifty chance of selecting the correct response and the fact that true–false items lack the diagnostic features of multiple-choice items. An incorrect response on a multiple-choice item can be analyzed and the source of the misconception can frequently be determined. A true or false response does not provide any information other than the obvious fact that the student does or does not know the correct answer.

Despite its limitations, the true–false item can provide an effective measurement whenever there are only two responses. Whenever a multiple-choice item is inappropriate or impossible to construct, a true–false item may be used. The criteria for good items must be followed strictly:

1. Each item should contain one and only one central idea.
2. The central idea must be worded precisely to permit unequivocal true–false judgment.
3. The items should be short and simply stated.

[3] Norman E. Gronlund, *Constructing Achievement Tests* (Englewood Cliffs, N.J.: Prentice-Hall, 1968), pp. 44–48.

4. Negative statements should be avoided. When a negative statement is used, the negative words should be emphasized.
5. Avoid providing clues, for example,
   a. Absolutes, such as *always*, *never*, *only*, and *all*, which all tend to make statements false.
   b. Qualifiers, such as *usually*, *generally*, *may*, and *sometimes*, which tend to make statements true.
   c. Too much length variation; true statements tend to be longer.
   d. A disproportionate number of one or another type of question.

Short-Answer Items

The short-answer, or completion, item is the only type of objective item which requires the student to supply, rather than select, an appropriate answer. The major disadvantage of this type of item is that it is difficult to construct questions or phrases which have only one correct answer. This format is useful for computational items and whenever a selection-type question would provide obvious clues. Because selection-type items which provide obvious clues generally attempt to measure trivial performance, substituting a short-answer item will not enhance the question quality. Restricting the use of the short-answer item to computational questions is advisable. Rules for constructing short-answer items include the following:

1. State the item so that a single correct answer is possible.
2. Use a direct question; avoid ambiguous, incomplete statements or phrases.
3. Restrict the response to include only the main point.
4. Place blanks at the end of the statement and not at the beginning or at some other point.
5. Avoid providing extraneous clues such as
   a. The use of *a* or *an* at the end of the statement.
   b. Answer-blank lengths which depict the size of the response desired.

Essay Items[4]

There are two general types of essay items. *Restricted-response* questions tend to limit both the content and form of student response. They can be used to ascertain whether the student can supply rather than merely recognize interpretations and applications of data. *Extended-response* questions permit

[4] Gronlund, *Measurement and Evaluation in Teaching*, pp. 180–93.

the student a wide range of freedom and can be used to measure the student's ability to select, organize, and integrate ideas pertinent to the solution of a problem. No other test item can measure these terminal performances.

In spite of the fact that essay items may provide a direct measure of significant terminal performances, they have several limitations which should restrict their use. Because essay items cannot measure adequately the full range of desired achievement, they should be used in conjunction with many other types of test items. Some of the important limitations of essay items are that

1. Scoring tends to be unreliable.
2. Scoring is very time-consuming.
3. A limited sampling of achievement is obtained.

The unreliable nature of essay items has been described in several studies and is by far the most serious limitation. Teachers tend to give lower scores to students if their paper contains grammar, punctuation, or spelling errors— even when they are directed to overlook these errors. Students who are clever writers will score significantly higher even if they know less. When more than one teacher grades an essay exam, the assigned grades frequently range from A to F on the same item. Even if the same teacher regrades an item, the probability that he will assign the same grade is very small.

The sampling error of essay exams must also be considered. Tests should be designed to sample student achievement for the simple reason that it should be impossible to measure the total achievement of three or more weeks of instruction within the confines of a single testing period. It takes much more time to supply information than to recognize and select appropriate responses. Thus, the sample of achievement a student can demonstrate on an essay examination is decidedly smaller than the amount of achievement he could demonstrate on a recognition–selection type of examination. This statement can be made even without exploring the assumption that three or four essay questions could be designed that would sample total achievement adequately if time were not a factor.

These arguments have not been advanced to discourage you from using essay items. Essay questions are essential in any balanced testing program. Their limitations should be recognized and their use restricted to appropriate situations. Some of their limitations can be controlled if care is taken in constructing and grading. Some suggested rules to follow when constructing essay items include the following:

1. Restrict the use of essay items to measuring only those terminal performances which cannot be measured by other means.
2. State the problem as specifically as possible.

3. Indicate a time limit.
4. Avoid providing optional questions; optional questions permit students to complete different tests which may not be comparable. Although permitting students to select the question they wish to answer may improve morale, it affects the validity of the instrument as an achievement measurement.

The reliability of an essay item can be improved by carefully designing the items and controlling the evaluation. Some steps to follow include those listed at the top of page 184.

Types of Complex Learning Outcomes Measured by Essay Questions and Objective Interpretive Exercises

Type of Test Item	Examples of Complex Learning Outcomes That Can Be Measured
Objective interpretive exercises	Ability to 　recognize cause-effect relationship 　recognize the application of principles 　recognize the relevance of arguments 　recognize tenable hypotheses 　recognize valid conclusions 　recognize unstated assumptions 　recognize the limitations of data 　recognize the adequacy of procedures (and similar outcomes based on the pupils' ability to *recognize* the answer)
Restricted-response essay questions	Ability to 　explain cause-effect relationships 　describe applications of principles 　present relevant arguments 　formulate tenable hypotheses 　formulate valid conclusions 　state necessary assumptions 　describe methods and procedures (and similar outcomes based on the pupils' ability to *supply* the answer)
Extended-response essay questions	Ability to 　produce, organize, and express ideas 　integrate learnings in different areas 　create original forms (e.g., designing an experiment) 　evaluate the worth of ideas

From Norman E. Gronlund, *Measurement and Evaluation in Teaching* (New York: Macmillan, 1967), p. 184. Reprinted by permission of The Macmillan Company.

1. Prepare a model answer in advance.
2. Use an appropriate scoring method; restricted-response questions may be scored by a point method which involves comparing each answer with the ideal answer and assigning a number of points in terms of the adequacy of the item. Extended-response questions should be scored by a rating method which involves placing the papers in one of three to five piles, representing degrees of quality, as they are read.
3. Evaluate all the answers to one question before going on to another.
4. Avoid looking at the student's name when evaluating the items.

The decision concerning the types of items utilized on an examination should be guided by the type of terminal performances being measured. The table on page 183, constructed by Gronlund, although merely suggestive of the full range of performances that should be measured, summarizes this point of view and the discussion of test item types.

Useful Statistics

The statistics most frequently employed by science teachers include measures of central tendency and measures of variability. Measures of central tendency include the mean, median, and mode. Examine the distribution of scores (X).

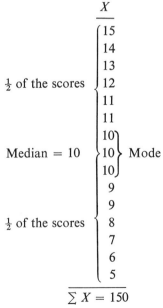

The sum of these raw scores ($\sum X$) is 150. The arithmetic mean (M) of these raw scores can be obtained by adding the scores ($\sum X$) and dividing the total by the number of scores (N).

$$\sum X = 150 \qquad \text{Mean} = M = \frac{\sum X}{N} = \frac{150}{15} = 10$$
$$N = 15$$

in which

$\sum$ = the sum of

X = any raw score

N = number of scores

$\sum X$ = the sum of the raw scores

In this example the mean is at the center of the distribution. How would a single very high or very low score influence the mean?

The *median* (Mdn) is the counting average. It can be determined by arranging the scores in order and counting up to (or down to) the halfway point. In this example an odd number of scores are present and the median is the middle score, 10. If there were an even number of scores in the distribution, the median would be halfway between the two middle-most scores. Because this is a counting average, 50 per cent of the scores are above the median and 50 per cent of the scores lie below the median. The median score is not affected by extreme scores.

The *mode* is the most frequent score in the distribution and it is determined by inspection. In the example the score 10 occurs three times and is thus the mode. The mode is the least accurate measure of central tendency.

Variability

The standard deviation (SD) is the most useful measure of variability. It is essentially an average of the degree to which a set of scores deviate from the mean. The usefulness of this measure is derived from the fact that it is the most commonly used measure of dispersion and the most dependable measure of variability, and it is used in a wide variety of statistical procedures.

Basically, the idea may be viewed as a means of obtaining a better estimate of the degree a given score deviates from the arithmetic mean. The procedure used to compute the SD is included in the following steps:

1. Compute the deviation (x) by subtracting the mean from each score.
2. Square each deviation (x^2).
3. Add the squares to obtain ($\sum x^2$).

4. Divide the $\sum x^2$ by N.
5. Determine the square root.

$$M = \frac{\sum X}{N} \qquad SD = \sqrt{\frac{\sum x^2}{N}}$$

	X	x	x^2
	15	+5	25
	14	+4	16
	13	+3	9
	12	+2	4
	11	+1	1
$N = 15$	11	+1	1
	10	0	0
	10	0	0
	10	0	0
	9	−1	1
	9	−1	1
	8	−2	4
	7	−3	9
	6	−4	16
	5	−5	25

$$\sum X = 150 \qquad \sum x^2 = 112$$

$$M = \frac{150}{15} = 10 \qquad SD = \sqrt{\frac{112}{15}} = \sqrt{7.47} = 2.7$$

A shortcut can be used to estimate the standard deviation which involves very little effort. This measurement is only an estimate of the standard deviation. Further calculation using the estimated standard deviation (SD^E) magnifies any error and must be avoided. Its major function is to provide the harried teacher a rapid and relatively accurate means of estimating the degree of dispersion and variability. The following formula summarizes how this estimate may be obtained:

$$SD^E = 2 \frac{(\text{Upper } \frac{1}{6} \text{ of the Scores} - \text{Lower } \frac{1}{6} \text{ of the Scores})}{N}$$

Simply computing standard deviations does not provide insight into their applicability, or meaning. The meaning of standard deviation becomes more apparent when it is explained in terms of the normal probability curve. (Also called the normal distribution curve, the normal curve, or the bell-shaped curve.) The normal distribution curve is a mathematical formulation. It does not occur in nature. It is not a biological, educational, or psychological curve. It is a model or ideal pattern which may be used to describe the chance occurrence of phenomena. The normal curve is a symmetrical, bell-shaped curve, the area under which may be divided into standard deviation units containing a fixed number of cases.

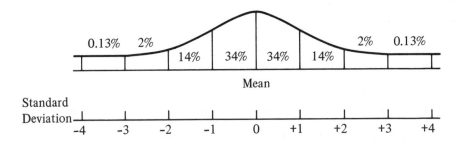

In the normal distribution, 34 per cent of the scores will be in the area beneath the curve between the mean and one standard deviation unit either way from the mean. Sixty-eight per cent of the scores will fall within ±1 SD of the mean. Twenty-eight per cent (14 on each side) of the scores will be in the areas beneath the curve between +1 and +2 SD and −1 and −2 SD. Four per cent (2 per cent on each side) of the scores will be in the areas beneath the curve between +2 and +3 SD and −2 and −3 SD. Only 0.13 per cent of the scores fall above or below ±3 SD. For all practical purposes a normal distribution of scores falls within + and − three standard deviations of the mean.

The normal curve and standard deviations can be used to compare the scores obtained by the same population of students on two different tests. Examine the two score distributions given in Table 14-1. The student's raw scores on these examinations are a function of the length of the examination and the average difficulty of the test items. These two exams cannot be directly compared because of the obvious difficulty difference.

For example, the raw score 50 is in the middle of the distribution on one test, whereas it lies at the end of the distribution on the other test. A direct comparison is possible if both scores are arranged along the base line of a normal distribution curve. A raw score of 25 on Test A and 72 on Test B are equal because both are one standard deviation unit below the mean. When this conversion to standard deviation scores is made, the raw scores are no

Table 14-1

A				B		
X	x	x^2		X	x	x^2
93	43	1,849	Distribution A	95	14	196
90	40	1,600		93	12	144
86	36	1,296	$M = \dfrac{\sum x}{N} = \dfrac{1,750}{35} = 50$	92	11	121
83	33	1,089		92	11	121
81	31	961	$SD = \dfrac{\sqrt{\sum x^2}}{N}$	90	9	81
79	29	841		89	8	64
78	28	784	$= \dfrac{\sqrt{21,192}}{35}$	88	7	49
75	25	625		88	7	49
73	23	529		87	6	36
69	19	361	$= \sqrt{602.63} = 24.5$	86	5	25
67	17	289		85	4	16
63	13	169	Distribution B	85	4	16
61	11	121		85	4	16
58	8	64	$M = \dfrac{\sum X}{N} = \dfrac{2,835}{35} = 81$	85	4	16
54	4	16		84	3	9
52	2	4	$SD = \sqrt{\dfrac{2,612}{35}}$	83	2	4
50	0	0		83	2	4
50	0	0	$= \sqrt{74.63} = 8.64$	83	2	4
50	0	0		82	1	1
48	-2	4		82	1	1
46	-4	16		80	-1	1
42	-8	64		80	-1	1
39	-11	121		79	-2	4
37	-13	169		78	-3	9
33	-17	289		77	-4	16
31	-19	361		76	-5	25
27	-23	529		75	-6	36
25	-25	625		75	-6	36
22	-28	784		74	-7	49
21	-29	841		73	-8	64
19	-31	961		73	-8	64
17	-33	1,089		70	-11	121
14	-36	1,296		69	-12	144
10	-40	1,600		68	-13	169
7	-43	1,849		51	-30	900
1,750 $\sum X$		21,192 $\sum x^2$		2,835 $\sum X$		2,612 $\sum x^2$

longer needed. A score of two standard deviations to the right of the mean on Test B is superior to a score of one standard deviation to the right on Test A, regardless of the average item difficulty or the length of the examination.

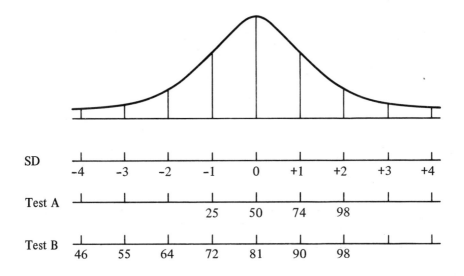

Utilizing the standard deviation to convert several sets of raw scores to a common scale with equal units can have a very practical application in the computation of grades. The standard score derived is a better indicator of a student's relative position in the class. Assume that a student received sixty-one points on Test A and ninety-two points on Test B. Both scores are eleven points above the mean and his average score (61 + 92)/2 is 76.5. Because both his scores were above average, we can conclude that he was achieving better than average. It is impossible to tell exactly how much because the 76.5 score was obtained by averaging two scores which could not be compared.

However, if the eleven points which the student scored above the mean were divided by the standard deviations of their distributions, directly comparable scores would be derived.

$$\begin{array}{cc} + \;.45 & + \;\; 1.29 \\ 24.5 \overline{\smash{)}11.0.00} & 8.64 \overline{\smash{)}11.00.00} \end{array}$$

These standard scores could be added and averaged. The derived score

$$\begin{array}{r} .45 \\ 1.29 \\ 2 \overline{\smash{)}1.74} \\ \hline +.87 \end{array}$$

indicates the relative position of the student more accurately. In this case the student is 0.87 standard deviations to the right of the class mean. The derived score illustrated here is called a Z-score, which is the simplest of the standard scores. The formula for computing Z-scores is

$$\text{Z-score} = Z = \frac{X - M}{SD}$$

where X = Raw Score

M = Mean

SD = Standard Deviation

The Z-score is always minus when the raw score is smaller than the mean. Examine the computation of two Z-scores for raw scores in Distribution B (Table 14-1).

$$Z = \frac{X - M}{SD} \qquad M = 81 \qquad SD = 8.6$$

$$Z = \frac{95 - 81}{8.6} = \frac{14}{8.6} = +1.6$$

$$Z = \frac{68 - 81}{8.6} = \frac{-13}{8.6} = -1.5$$

The Z-score, 1.6, would be 1.6 standard deviation units to the right of the mean. The Z-score, -1.5, would be 1.5 standard deviations below the mean. Forgetting a minus sign would cause a serious error in test interpretation. Rather than run this risk, Z-scores are usually transformed into standard scores which utilize only positive numbers. T-scores are a specific type of standard scores designed to eliminate the use of negative numbers. To determine a T-score, multiply the Z-score by 10 and add the product to 50.

$$\text{T-score} = 50 + (Z)(10)$$

$$T = 50 + (1.6)(10) = 66 \text{ (for raw score of 95)}$$

$$T = 50 + (-1.5)(10) = 35 \text{ (for raw score of 68)}$$

This formula affects the Z-score by moving the decimal point one place to the right, removing all negative numbers, defining the mean as 50, and establishing the standard deviation unit as 10. A T-score of 65 is always 1.5 standard deviation units above the mean. The fixed mean (50) and standard deviation unit (10) make interpretation of these scores very easy.

Many other standard scores are computed from Z-scores. They differ only in the values used for means and standard deviation units. The Graduate Record Examination and the examinations of the College Entrance Examination Board have means of 500 and standard deviations of 100. A score of 600 on a C.E.E.B. examination could be interpreted as a T-score of 60, indicating that the student was one standard deviation to the right of the mean. Deviation I.Q. scores have a mean of 100 and a standard deviation unit of 16. A person one standard deviation unit below the mean would have a deviation I.Q. of 84, which could be expressed as a T-score of 40. The following figure illustrates the similarity of these types of scores.[5]

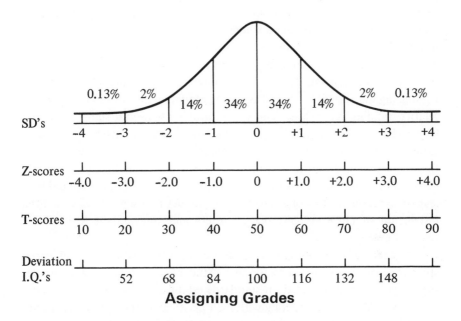

Assigning Grades

Normal curve statistics can be very useful to describe the progress of students in relation to other members of their class. A few precautionary comments are needed, however, because the normal curve was not designed as a panacea for assigning grades.

The appropriateness of using normal curve statistics and the normal curve to assign grades is questionable. The distribution represented by the normal curve adequately describes chance or random activities. Instruction is, or should be, purposeful activity; it attempts to get students to learn what we have to teach. The postinstruction distribution of scores should vary from

[5] After Gronlund, with permission of The Macmillan Company.

the normal curve. The extent of the variance from normal may be the best indication of the effectiveness of the instruction. This statement is particularly true if attempts are being made to individualize instruction.

Bloom indicates that the normal curve has been in use for so long that everyone, teachers and students, believes in it.[6] Accepting the normal curve as "a truth" has led teachers and students to assume that approximately one third of the students will fail or barely pass, one third of the students will learn the material adequately, and one third of the students will learn a lot but not enough to be classified as good students. This set of expectations, accepted by the school and transmitted through grading policies to all its participants, severely inhibits achievement. The majority, and perhaps 90 per cent of the students in the secondary school, could probably master the material presented at the "good student" level. It is the teacher's task to find means which will enable students to master the content and to avoid mechanistic procedures which inhibit or prohibit achievement.

Bloom recommends eliminating the interstudent competition established by utilizing the normal curve and assigning grades on the basis of the student's relative standing in the class.[7] This would mean that absolute standards would have to be established and that grades and marks would have to reflect these standards. It must also mean that all students could get an A if they achieve the mastery level. If aptitude, which frequently correlates highly with a student's grade under present systems, is only the amount of time required by a learner to attain mastery of a learning task, modern systems of individualized instruction should eventually place mastery and concomitant A's into the reach of every student.[8]

A means of eliminating interstudent competition, which has influenced student mastery, is reported by Bloom.[9] Students were told that their grades for the year would be based on standards established the year before. That is, they would not be competing with their classmates; their grade would not be determined by their relative position in class; they would be judged on the basis of levels of mastery used the previous year. The results reported were phenomenal. In one class, where 20 per cent of the students had received a grade of A in the previous year, the A's reported for the year involving the study were 80 per cent. That is, 80 per cent of the students mastered the content at the A level.

[6] Benjamin S. Bloom, J. Thomas Hastings, George F. Madaus, *Formative and Summative Evaluation of Student Learning* (New York: McGraw-Hill, 1970).

[7] Ibid.

[8] John Carroll, "A Model of School Learning," *Teachers College Record*, Vol. 64 (1963), pp. 723–33.

[9] Bloom et al., op. cit.

The strategy did involve a little more than simply informing the students that they were competing *only* with themselves. It involved designing programs with alternate paths, diagnostic criterion tests, and specifically informing students where they were weak and how they might correct these weaknesses. Basically their strategy included

1. Breaking the content into small pieces and arranging them in a hierarchical sequence (task analysis).
2. Describing to students, in specific measurable terms, exactly what they should be able to do.
3. Evaluating students in terms of the criteria stated in the performance objectives.
4. Providing feedback to the students concerning their performance on the examinations and specifically indicating to them how to correct any deficiency.

Changes other than achievement were noted. These included the increased willingness of students to work with and help each other and a general improvement of their attitude toward learning.

The authors admit that many experiments patterned after Bloom's work will fail. The failures will generally be a function of our inability to define specifically significant terminal outcomes, arrange learning in hierarchical steps, and give specific direction to a floundering student; failures are not the result of the inappropriateness of the idea.

The authors also concede that this idea is going to be very hard to sell to a tradition-bound system which has accepted the ideas that aptitude equals achievement and that only a few students can really master the content. If the school hopes to prepare students for their role in a modern society which requires continual learning throughout life, it must prepare students who know they can learn. This means that the vast majority of students must be led to believe in themselves as students who can master material. This is the only type of student who can develop the necessary life-long interest in learning.

Unfortunately many readers of this text will discover that the system of teaching and grading described by Bloom cannot be applied in their particular teaching situation because too many teachers and administrators still believe that the full range of scores (A to F) should be used. It is hoped that the teachers who see the merit of Bloom's system will begin encouraging their colleagues to rethink their grading philosophies. Until the desired change in grading philosophy can be made, it may be necessary to use a more traditional scheme. The problem then becomes one of applying the traditional comparative scheme in as positive a manner as possible.

Using raw scores is one of the commonest errors committed by teachers. Raw scores *should not* be added or averaged, because raw scores on different tests are not comparable. Standard scores such as the ones illustrated earlier in this chapter can be averaged; furthermore, a standard score is not a function of either the length of the examination or the average difficulty of the test items. If a system utilizing standard scores were used, the following distribution might be appropriate for a below-average class.

	Z-Score	Standard Score	Standard Deviations
A's	1.5 and above	65 and above	Scores above +1.5 SD's
B's	0.5 to 1.49	55 to 64	Scores from 0.5 to 1.5 SD's
C's	−0.5 to 0.49	45 to 54	Scores between −0.5 and +0.5 SD's
D's	−1.5 to −0.49	35 to 44	Scores from −1.5 to −0.5 SD's
F's	below −1.5	below 35	Scores below −1.5 SD's

Following this plan for a below-average class would produce a full range of scores. Some teachers will, of course, state that the slow or below-average students should not receive A's or B's. Urge them to label the course rather than the child. Some of the students in the below-average classes may discover that they can learn if they are given the positive motivation of an A grade.

In average and above-average classes the following plan may be appropriate.

	Z-Scores	Standard Scores
A's	1.0 and above	60 and above
B's	0.0 to 0.99	50 to 59
C's	−0.01 to −1.0	40 to 49
D's	−1.01 to −2.0	30 to 39
F's	Below −2.0	Below 30

This plan may be appropriate for most regular biology classes. In many schools chemistry and physics as well as honors science courses are only taken by the higher achievers. Whenever enrollment in these courses is restricted to the very bright, an even more liberal grading plan should be used. The two plans presented are only examples of how assigning grades on a relative basis can be handled mechanically. No attempt was made to justify either plan.

What About F's?

Many teachers feel that they are forced to fail students by the school system or by a student who refuses to learn an acceptable amount of material. A student who does not learn an acceptable amount probably should be retained until an acceptable amount is learned. However, if you accept this idea, you must define what is meant by the term *acceptable amount*. The fact that secondary school students, even slow students, are learning much more than did their parents must be a consideration. An acceptable amount cannot be defined as just a little more than the amount learned by the two lowest achievers in the class.

Most students who fail a course are convinced that they cannot succeed in the course and unless their attitude is changed the chance that they will do significantly better when they repeat it is greatly diminished. In fact, they generally do not achieve as much in their second exposure as they did in their first. As such, before a student is failed, the teacher should be able to state emphatically that the student will profit from his second experience in that class.

Discussion Questions

1. If you assume that aptitude is only a measure of the amount of time required by a learner to attain mastery of a learning task, how should you want to change instructional practices?
2. Can you support the assumption stated in question 1 with personal experiences? Relate and explain.
3. How might you use grades to influence learning positively?
4. Argue, pro or con, "Grading should be abolished!"
5. If 90 per cent of the students receive A's, does that mean that 90 per cent of the students should go to college?

Additional References

Diederich, P. *Short-Cut Statistics for Teacher-Made Tests.* Princeton, N.J.: Educational Testing Service, 1960.

Dizney, Henry. *Classroom Evaluation for Teachers*. Dubuque, Ia.: William C. Brown Publishing Company, 1971.

Gorow, Frank F. *Better Classroom Testing*. Belmont, Calif.: Chandler Publishing Company, 1968.

Gronlund, Norman E. *Readings in Measurement and Evaluation: Education and Psychology*. New York: The Macmillan Company, 1968.

Little, J. Maxwell. *An Introduction to the Experimental Method*. Minneapolis: Burgess Publishing Co., 1961.

extracurricular activities

This chapter is concerned with the description and rationale for extracurricular learning activities of science students. Let us at the outset attempt to clarify some alternatives: to require or not to require an "extra" involvement of science students. A thing required is actually a part of the curriculum and not really extra. An "extra" yet required involvement may be like a "custom" car which is mass-produced and available to the general public. Such an involvement is likely to be seen by students as just another activity in the standard curriculum. Although it may be used to provide some opportunity to develop students' ability to operate independently of the teacher, it is not known whether the students would have decided to become involved if they were free not to.

The activities discussed below will be of a voluntary sort. To enter into such an activity, the student will be the decision maker, and his participation may afford the teacher an opportunity to study his preferences in and attitudes toward science and enable a description of his skills in situations where he is likely to make optimum use of them.

Finally, the facilitation of voluntary activities deserves serious consideration by the teacher if only because these activities are fun for students and may enable student identification with the school in situations closer to life than those found in the compulsory curriculum.

Voluntary science activities might be classified in several ways. For convenience we shall divide them into the categories of (1) the science club, (2) reports to teacher and/or class, (3) science projects and "fairs."

The Science Club as a voluntary activity may have several attributes which can be used to justify its existence. Any school club can be defended if it affords leadership practice and the socialization of students through some sort of participatory democratic experience. Additionally, a subject-matter-related club (science) is expected to have affective or attitudinal objectives aimed at appreciating and valuing the discipline concerned and the activities of professionals within it. A science club may offer the only opportunity an interested student has to obtain further (than the classroom) guidance in investigating the nature of science.

Club organization ranges from the form of an elite seminar to a casual meeting of students for low-pressure discussion and action. Intended for the "gifted" student, many seminar types of clubs assume (1) that the "gifted" can be identified reliably and (2) that they need to be segregated. There may be a need to question these and other assumptions which lead us to institutionalize, on any criteria with school sanction, the segregation of children. If defended and maintained, this kind of club requires the artful cooperation of sponsor and members to build a challenging program which will not degenerate into a series of college survey-course lectures or occupation-oriented talks with local professional and technical people.

For the present we shall concern ourselves with the regular, nonelite, or general science club. It may be that the central purpose of such a club is to broaden the science experiential background of students, for example, to provide an environment which responds to student questions about natural phenomena, methods of investigating them, and careers in questioning and investigating. A science club's activities may also sample broadly across the disciplines to answer such questions as, "What do __ologists, __ists, and __icians do?" "Why do they do what they do?"

Two factors are worth designation as "principles of effective club establishment." In organizing a club to meet objectives similar to the preceding, the sponsor or some equivalent organizer initially should provide procedural structure which frees members to work toward the objectives and should be wary of hyperorganizationalism. Students enroll in a voluntary club without knowing what they are getting into. Plan some initial activities in advance and at all times model for them the kind of club member you are trying to develop. Clubs are not formal classrooms, but the members will still look to their sponsor, as "teacher," to set the limits of objectivity and informality. Secondly, try not to yield to the tendency of some "club types" to turn the proceedings into miniature student government sessions complete with more officers, rules, and points of order than a political convention.

Once established, these limits and resistance to clubmanship work in favor of the sponsor's ultimate goal: yielding reasoned leadership to the members. This requires that, in the extreme, a sponsor's role will become one of mere presence to satisfy legal requirements of adult participation when children are in the school. Ideally, a sponsor who has modeled responsible and successful leadership toward a club's objectives may find members voluntarily assuming leadership roles to become more deeply involved. When motivation is high, a successful sponsor takes this opportunity to involve members in leadership and at the same time decreases his own influence. This relinquishment of reasoned authority is a delicate procedure somewhat analogous to a shift from a benevolent monarchy to a republican democracy overseen by a king who wishes to abdicate and remain in his country as an observer and "common" citizen. He wishes to become a citizen-observer of reasoned government, moving the country toward goals that all citizens value. In the same sense, a club sponsor seeks to "lose his job" as he manipulates a club toward member direction and serves as a true advisor only when his professional advice is sought by others. Such a club is well worth the effort and, we submit, far more satisfying to sponsor than a year-long *ein fuehrer, ein volk* situation.

It is worthwhile to involve parents for assistance whenever feasible. Many parents have already distinguished themselves as chauffeurs for various reasons in addition to daily pick-up and delivery service at the school door. It has been our experience that parents who have ferried clubs to various excursion places have usually become interested and involved in the activities themselves and are pleased to help the club at future times. Interested parents have lent their garages, basements, rowboats, tools, and muscle to aid science clubs voluntarily engaged in activities. It is important to communicate the club's and sponsor's objectives to these parents. They will appreciate that their children are being given responsibility for leadership of a special interest club and will not be as likely to be directive or otherwise tend toward decision making which belongs to the members. In the final analysis these involved parents are more likely to support your instructional program and school in general. Everyone benefits from parental assistance to the science club.

An important consideration with regard to *voluntary reports* to the teacher and/or class is evaluation. When a student submits some piece of work outside of the standard course requirements, it may not be necessary to "grade" it unless he has asked specifically for this type of evaluation. One either assigns grades for norm–comparative purposes or as a "pass–fail" indication of having or not having reached some criterion performance. With reference to this first purpose, no other student was required to turn in a comparable piece of work, so your voluntary population may be of very small size and influenced by variance in work-piece topic or methods, in which case norms would be difficult to construct or defend. In the second class of grading purpose you could not have predicted the nature of all voluntary projects so accurately that you would have been able to set, in advance, some type of performance to a criterion of success or failure. Is there any instance when grading is defensible for this type of effort? Let us shift back from use of the term *grade* to *evaluate*. This allows us to get away from considerations of letters or numbers. And one might now think of a voluntary worker's position along some continuum of affect or attitude development. In this situation the teacher's responsibility becomes one of determining the proper reinforcing communication to make to one whose values are still developing. Although the teacher may certainly keep records on the inferred effect that the volunteer work has had on a given student's attitudinal or criterial bias development, his only evaluational remarks to the student should be to provide the reinforcement necessary to maintain such affective change. It is questionable whether letters or numbers can do this by themselves. This is also true if the student asks for an evaluation of his work. There is no way of determining if the student who asks is less shy or more achievement conscious than the student who does not ask and who may be shy or unconcerned about a grade on his outside interest or hobby which would have persisted with or without science class. Forget motives. Be glad to receive these efforts as opportunities to help *any* student develop attitudes and values,[1,2] and do not use any record of them to color the school-required final course grade. If volunteerism is significant to affective growth and if affective qualities promote cognitive aims, then such work may have its effect on course outcomes without grade tampering along the way. We suggest holding these deductions as assumptions until significant evidence to the contrary is available.

The English department has the school play, the physical education department has the athletic teams, and the science department has the *science fair*. Love it or deplore it, the science fair in some form or another is nearly

[1] D. R. Krathwohl, B. S. Bloom, and B. Masia, *A Taxonomy of Educational Objectives, Handbook II: The Affective Domain* (New York: David McKay). (A detailed treatment of affective objectives as they apply to school in general.)

[2] Richard M. Bingman (ed.), "Inquiry Objectives in the Teaching of Biology." McREL Position Paper, Vol. 1, No. 1 (September, 1969). Mid-continent Regional Educational Laboratory; 104 East Independence Avenue; Kansas City, Missouri 64106. (Chapter 5 in the BSCS-McREL document deals specifically with affective or attitudinal qualities of inquiry behaviors.)

as widely accepted a secondary school extracurricular institution as plays and games. At this point we shall accept and defend "fair"-type projects, and we shall do so within the limits of educational objectives. That is, insomuch as voluntary participation in project work (which may or may not include a "fair" exhibit and the complex technicalities of adult judging and prize awards) furthers the development of self-direction of learning or inquiry and maintains or develops scientific attitudes, such work is good. And students who show an inclination toward it should be encouraged.

To the degree that teacher or other intrusion removes the "self" from direction and to the degree that compulsion to participate or *other* factors stop or reverse attitudinal development, this activity is bad. Nearly any criticism of the science-fair tradition can be traced to one of the preceding, or related, abuses. A few of the *other* factors referred to are overemphasis on petty competition; awards on the criterion of displaymanship; incompetent and/or inconsistent judging to select "winners"; the use of children as public relations pawns to buy community favor; systems of local, district, regional, and national "runoffs" which involve schools and students in yet another organizational hierarchy of rules, lines, and numbers; teacher possession of misinformation, little information, or even fear of a content area in which a student seeks counsel; lack of teacher preparedness to counsel *generally*, even though he may have graduate degrees in a particular content area.

Despite the pros and cons large numbers of science fairs attract the participation of students every year, voluntarily or otherwise. If we assume for the sake of investigation that science-fair awards (success) do reflect some measure of self-direction and that the recipients may be more likely to develop scientific attitudes than nonrecipients (both assumptions are quite broad, considering the variance in conditions across thousands of schools), we may profit by an examination of achievement or skill correlations with fair success. The profit might depend on the hypothesis that correlations could help predict success or even allow us to help students become more successful. These assumptions and the possibility that relationships of certain factors to science-fair success could become an educational tool source have prompted research into science fairs and their participants.

A study by Bingman[3] of the aptitudes and interests of tenth-grade science-fair participants enrolled in high schools in an eastern area with a strong science-fair tradition revealed no significant differences, except for clerical aptitude, between winners and nonwinners on the basis of any of the

---

[3] Richard M. Bingman, *Aptitude and Interest Profiles of Tenth Grade Biology Students Participating in the Montgomery County, Pennsylvania Science Fairs (1962–1966)*, unpublished doctoral dissertation, Temple University, Philadelphia.

subscores of the *Differential Aptitude Test*[4] or the *Kuder Preference Record, Vocational*.[5] Winners were more able to perform routine clerical tasks quickly and accurately. However, many more findings of significance were recorded from a comparison of participants with nonparticipants. Interest in science, choice of science-related careers, scholastic aptitude, aptitude and preference for using numbers, aptitude for theoretical understandings, preference for discovery of new facts and solutions to problems, ability to perform routine (clerical) perceptual tasks, and *low* interest in artistic activities were all positively related to participation in science fairs.

Although these relationships are not concluded to be causal, and therefore may not indicate anything other than characteristics of certain students at a particular time in their lives, the finding of only one significant difference between winning and nonwinning participants might stimulate some hypothesizing as to the effect of fairlike competition on the development of students. Does participation *alone* generate enough motivation to cause the student to take part in these activities? Do nonparticipants fail to become involved because of project work, competition, or lack of some important ability or interest?

If any sort of individual or group research participation, fair related or otherwise, is to be encouraged as a voluntary extracurricular activity, much can be done by the teacher to optimize chances for the experience being a rewarding one. If the experience is to be truly student directed, what shall be the teacher's role? Obviously a minimum of teacher interference would be allowable during actual student design and execution of research attempts. Less obvious is the part the teacher plays in building skills for and predispositions toward research. Whenever, throughout the year, the teacher plans for the class such experiences as inquiry sessions involving actual problem formulation and research planning, the execution of laboratory work which follows a *real need to gather specific data to answer specific questions*, or the analysis and evaluation of actual research reports written by professionals or students, the teacher is helping students to acquire skills and attitudes needed to initiate and carry out their own investigations. Preparation for self-direction of learning may be seen as a rationale for educational objectives which the preceding experiences are designed to help achieve.

Once involved in a self-initiated research attempt the student may ask for advice regarding facilities, equipment, needed skills, and so on. His teacher should be willing to assist when asked. But *decisions* belong to the

---

[4] *Differential Aptitude Tests,* 4th ed. (New York: The Psychological Corporation, 1966).
[5] *Kuder Preference Record, Vocational Forms C–H* (Chicago: Science Research Associates, 1959).

student who deserves the opportunity to follow them and realize their consequences.

The Educational Policies Commission of the National Education Association has listed seven underlying values of science. (Hawkins has called them virtues rather than values.[6] The reader may wish to consider them as such. Values or virtues, these seven characteristics seem to describe the disposition of science toward the environment, and, most importantly, the self-critical qualities of this disposition.[7]) They are

1. Longing to know and to understand.
2. Questioning of all things.
3. Search for data and their meaning.
4. Demand for verification.
5. Respect for logic.
6. Consideration of premises.
7. Consideration of consequences.

Although usually thought to require some measure of skills reflective of and values consistent with the first three categories, science project work also offers an opportunity to expose a student's thinking processes and products to his peers and thereby help him refine his strategy. Task-oriented scientists continually expose their work to the professional community for evaluation. They seek tests for hypotheses and audiences for the results of tests. Negative as well as positive aspects of criticism have value to a report writer. Professional analysis of reports reveals inconsistencies and enables the reporter to refine his attack as much as the report itself may aid the work of some other scientist. Criticism is seen as "thing-oriented" rather than as directed personally at the "good" or "bad" scientist. Similarly, a scientist's ego is not destroyed by the results of a well-executed experiment. That is, both support and rejection of hypotheses under test help narrow the focus of inquiry.

Students also can learn that exposure of their notions to test and of their conclusions to other students can aid their inquiry and that both passive and active reactions to their efforts can aid in decision making when moving on in their work. (The words *passive* and *active* are used here as one alternative to *good* and *bad*. This is meant to keep our focus away from personalities and on data.)

The preceding may suggest that rather than (or in addition to) formal

[6] D. Hawkins, "Education and the Spirit of Science," *The Science Teacher* (September, 1966).
[7] Educational Policies Commission, *Education and the Spirit of Science* (Washington, D.C.: National Education Association, 1966).

terminal adult "judging" of student projects, what is needed is regular exposure of progress and conclusions to peers. Scientists *demand* verification and seek criticism by the scientific community. The student research community is a more natural one to take this exposure than the adult community. Specifically, this is so because the student audience can benefit from the practice of criticism as much as the exposer can utilize their analysis. The student community operates and communicates within common limits of sophistication with respect to interpersonal relations and content-process understanding. This suggests that they are the likely ones to criticize their own research, or at least participate in a critical analysis on an equivalent basis with teachers or other adults. It is well to recall that we are discussing *voluntary* research which supplements the compulsory curriculum, and not, *at least on this occasion*, suggesting student management of course evaluation in general.

The following constitute a summary of suggestions for the utilization of strategies and resources to encourage research participation.

1. Provide opportunities for students to understand the nature of laboratory work as investigation rather than as mere execution of someone else's "exercises" at an arbitrary time.
2. Allow students to read and analyze actual research reports.
3. Create stituations in which students must define problems and plans of attack at their solution.
4. Allow students to analyze each other's thought and work while emphasizing the constructive effects of any objective criticism students offer.
5. Show respect for student decisions and allow students to experience the consequences.

Previously unmentioned are some logistical considerations.

1. Arrange for a place in the classroom or elsewhere where student materials may remain undisturbed when brought to school or assembled there.
2. Make material storage areas available to students who are willing to follow rules related to storage, checkout, and use.
3. Compile a list of "consultants" in and outside the school with whom you have talked who may give advice in specific disciplines to student researchers *while not interfering with opportunities for self-direction.*
4. Make a defensible decision as to whether or not to make available to

volunteer researchers a "fair" in the traditional sense,[8] with adult judges, and prizes. Weigh each aspect of such activities against your goals for student scientific attitudinal and rational skills development.

Discussion Questions

1. Is there a case for compulsory science extracurricular activity? Explain.
2. Is there a defense for awarding "extra credit" for voluntary extracurricular activity? Explain.
3. Which hobbies or interests do you have which indicate that you have an extracurricular science life?

Additional References

Moore, Shirley (ed.). *Science Projects Handbook.* New York: Ballantine Books, Inc., 1970.

National Science Teachers Association. *Award Winning FSA Science Projects.* Washington, D.C.: National Education Association, 1968. (For more information about Future Scientists of America clubs write to Dorothy Culbert, Student Programs, NSTA, 1201 Sixteenth Street, N.W., Washington, D.C. 20036.)

Ruchlis, Hy. *Guide to Science Projects.* New York: Book-Lab, Inc., 1968.

Stevens, R. A. *Out of School Science Activities for Young People.* New York: Unipub, Inc., 1970.

[8] For a comprehensive historical review of the science-fair tradition and the relationship of interests, aptitudes, and abilities to science success in and out of school and in occupations, the reader is directed to the following unpublished theses: R. M. Bingman, op. cit.; Ernest Burkman, "An Analytical Study of Factors Contributing to the Development of Projects Exhibited in the 1961 Florida Regional and State Science Fairs," unpublished doctoral dissertation, The University of Michigan, 1962; Gert L. Daniels, "Occupational Choices of Former Science Fair Exhibitors," unpublished doctoral dissertation, Columbia University, 1960; S. Stone, "The Contributions of Intelligence, Interests, Temperament and Certain Personality Variables to Academic Achievement in a Physical Science and Mathematics Curriculum," unpublished doctoral dissertation, New York University, 1957.

science facilities

Science teachers are often asked to participate in the planning of a new school building or the remodeling of an existing one. They see this planning opportunity as a real challenge because they realize how directly the science facility can influence science instruction. "How many utilities?" "How much and what kind of space will be needed for tomorrow's science instruction?" and "Can the school district afford the type of science facility we would like?" are questions asked by the teacher planners who realize that a single room may be used for the instruction of at least 7,500 students (50 years × 150 students per year).

This chapter is not designed to answer questions but to explore with you some general ideas which should facilitate your thinking. The chapter provides brief discussions of planning, space and utility requirements, plans and photographs of science facilities, and furniture found to be functional by science teachers.

The types of space needed for adequate science instruction can be classified as space for major instructional activities, space for ancillary instructional activities, and space for storage.

    A. Space for major instructional activities.

        1. Large-group instruction.

        2. Small-group instruction.

      3. Individual instruction.
      4. Laboratories.
   B. Space for ancillary instructional activities.
      1. Darkroom.
      2. Animal room.
      3. Green house.
      4. Planetarium.
      5. Project areas.
      6. Preparation areas.
      7. Office space.
   C. Storage.
      1. Supplies.
      2. Equipment.
      3. Student project work.

Utilities

It is often economically impossible and certainly impractical to make architectural modifications on a completed building. Adding electrical service or plumbing to an existing building is considerably more expensive than the original installation cost would have been. Furthermore, because it is frequently impossible to hide the additional pipes and wires within walls and floors, they will detract from the beauty of the building. Hence, it is essential to plan utility needs carefully, and it may even be wise to include more utilities than the planned instruction seems to demand. Each science room should have the following utilities. (Minimal quantity is described.)

   1. Electricity (150-amp service with many accessible outlets).
   2. Gas (one gas outlet for each pair of students plus at least five extra outlets).
   3. Hot and cold water (one sink for each four students plus two or three larger sinks).
   4. Compressed air (one air outlet for each pair of students plus at least five additional outlets).

Planning a Science Facility

Planning is at least a three-step operation. The initial step should include outlining instructional objectives and describing the space and utility require-

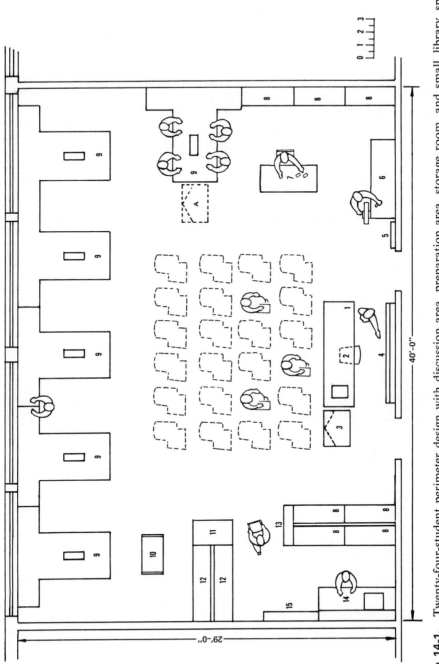

Figure 14-1. Twenty-four-student perimeter design with discussion area, preparation area, storage room, and small library space (1,160 sq. ft. total; 48 sq. ft. per student). (Courtesy of Kewaunee Technical Furniture Company; Statesville, N.C.)

Figure 14-2. Twenty-four-student design with storage preparation area, small project space, and room for a small library (1,315 sq. ft.; 54 sq. ft. per student). (Courtesy of Kewaunee Technical Furniture Company; Statesville, N.C.)

210

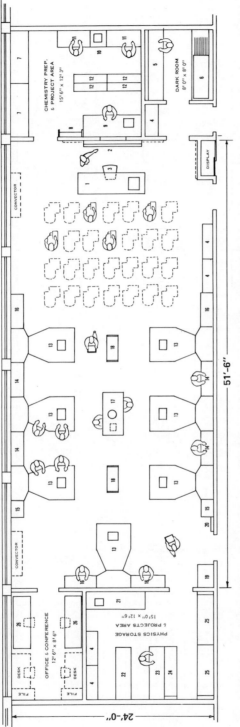

Figure 14-3. Twenty-eight-student chemistry-physics room. Also appropriate for biology, general science, or earth science (1,236 sq. ft.; 44 sq. ft. per student). (Courtesy of Kewaunee Technical Furniture Company; Statesville, N.C.)

212

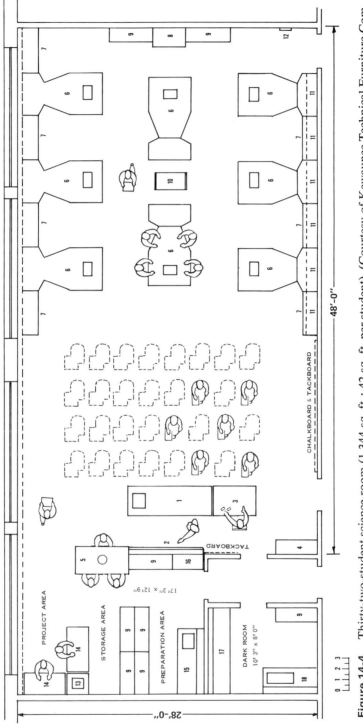

Figure 14-4. Thirty-two-student science room (1,344 sq. ft.; 42 sq. ft. per student). (Courtesy of Kewaunee Technical Furniture Company; Statesville, N.C.)

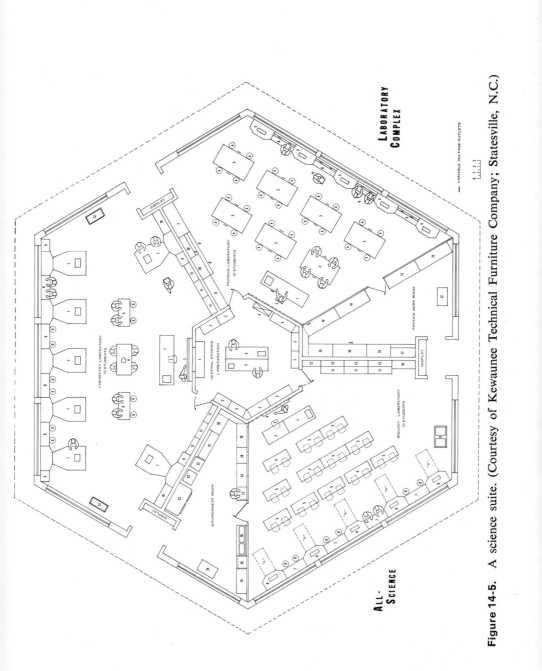

Figure 14-5. A science suite. (Courtesy of Kewaunee Technical Furniture Company; Statesville, N.C.)

ments which would facilitate the instruction inferred by the objectives. When the initial step is complete and only when the initial step is complete, a detailed examination of existing facilities and plans should be conducted. This study should include visiting schools and discussing various designs with both the designers and individuals who are teaching in them.

After completing steps 1 and 2, you should be prepared to help design a facility which your community can afford and in which a good science program can be developed. At this stage it may be appropriate to design three plans—a *poverty plan*, an *adequate plan*, and an *ideal plan*. If you plan carefully, these plans may be executed over several years without the excessive costs usually faced when additions to existing buildings are made. For example, initially your community may not be able to afford the electrical outlets, gas and compressed air outlets, or sinks listed as minimal utilities for a science room. If the air, gas, and electrical lines are brought to the room, providing outlets for them into the room at a later date may be feasible.

The remaining pages of this chapter are devoted to describing some existing plans and some design ideas which may assist you in planning a new facility or modifying an existing facility. The descriptions are sequenced in the following order: laboratory plans, plans for large science-study centers, carrels, and some portable furniture.

Large Science-Study Centers

Large science-study centers designed to facilitate a wide variety of science laboratory experiences are now commonly included in the design of new schools. Schools that have flexible modular scheduling find the large study center particularly useful. The basic idea of a large science center is portrayed in Figure 14-6.

The large science-study centers are designed to provide a wide variety of work space for approximately 100 students who may enter and leave the center any time of the day. The center might be staffed by two to five science teachers and a paraprofessional technician whose prime responsibility is laboratory maintenance.

The student using the center would enter one of the doors and go to the storeroom. In the storeroom the student would check in by giving a time-experience card to a teacher or paraprofessional. At this time the student would receive directions to proceed to a work space. Sometimes he may be directed to a carrel, the library, or a station where the materials he needs are already set up. At other times, the student would be given a box containing

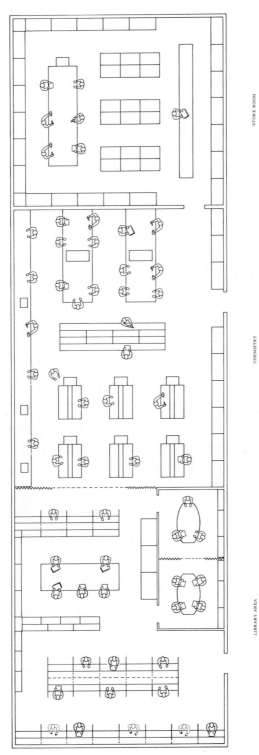

Figure 14-6. Science-study center. (Courtesy of Kewaunee Technical Furniture Company; Statesville, N.C.)

215

the material he needs and would be directed to an unoccupied work area. When the student completes his work or must go to another class or study center, he will check out of the science-study center by again picking up his time-experience card.

The teacher or paraprofessional in the storeroom would collect the time-experience cards and direct the student to a place to work. The card is then placed on a master board which permits the area assigner to see at a glance which areas of the laboratory are being used. The teachers working in the laboratory assist individuals who are having difficulty setting up equipment, following directions, or interpreting data.

Figure 14-7. Study center (Courtesy of Kewaunee Technical Furniture Company; Statesville, N.C.)

The general idea of a science-study center is depicted in Figure 14-6. Figures 14-7 and 14-8 portray two possible arrangements for small rooms (five students). Figure 14-9 shows a science classroom area built around a large science-study center.

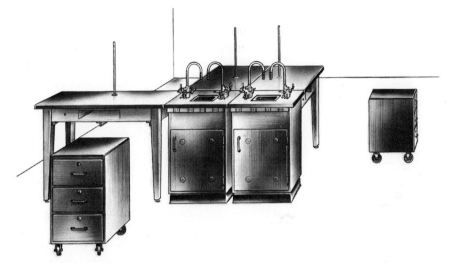

Figure 14-8. Science-study center. (Courtesy of Kewaunee Technical Furniture Company; Statesville, N.C.)

Flexible Student Study Carrels

The flexible study carrels illustrated in Figure 14-10 and similar designs can be used wherever space exists for their installation. The carrels illustrated were designed for a variety of purposes. The simplest design is a basic library unit. More complex units are equipped with storage space, gas, and water as well as electricity. The gas and water for these units are contained in re-fillable tanks located beneath the counter. The sink drain opens into a waste basket. If the gas, water, and drains were connected permanently, the units would demand much less maintenance. However, the fact that the units are equipped with the portable sources of gas and water means that they can be moved any place and installed without the expense of installing plumbing. This advantage should make these units highly desirable to schools with small budgets as well as schools that do not wish to ruin the appearance of their school by adding drain pipes after construction is completed.

Portable Furniture

The portable furniture examined by the authors was well constructed and should last many years with proper care. Although it may not last as long

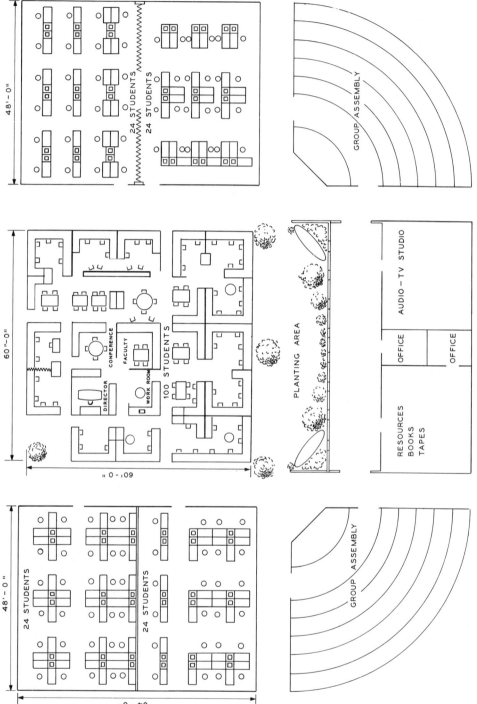

Figure 14-9. Large science-study center. (Courtesy of Kewaunee Technical Furniture Company; Statesville, N.C.)

Figure 14-10. Flexible study carrels. (Courtesy of Creative Educational Enterprises, Inc.; Cleveland, Ohio.)

Figure 14-11. Portable laboratory tables. (Courtesy of Creative Educational Enterprises, Inc.; Cleveland, Ohio.)

as permanently installed laboratory facilities, it does have other advantages. Flexibility is the first and primary advantage. Almost any room can be turned into a science laboratory by adding good work tables, water, gas, and electricity. Portable furniture can be rearranged or even moved to another room with little effort. The ease of installation is the second principal advantage. Because the portable units are equipped with gas and water, plumbing is not required; thus the cost of installation can be much lower. In spite of these obvious advantages, it cannot be said that these portable units are better than a permanently installed laboratory with seemingly endless supplies of gas and water. See Figure 14-11 for some examples of some portable laboratory tables.

Additional References

CUEBS. *Guidelines for Planning Biological Facilities.* Washington, D.C.: Commission on Undergraduate Education in the Biological Sciences, American Institute of Biological Sciences, 1968.

Gruss, Ronald, and Judith Murphy. *Educational Change and Architectural Consequence.* New York: Educational Facilities Laboratories, Inc., 1968.

Irving, James R. *How to Provide for Safety in the Science Laboratory.* Washington, D.C.: National Science Teachers Association, n.d.

National Institute of Health. *Laboratory Design Notes.* Bethesda, Md.: U.S. Department of Health, Education & Welfare. (NIH publishes a whole series of bulletins under this title; subjects range from Animal Care Equipment to the Design of Laboratory Buildings.)

15

planning your future in science teaching

College seniors are faced by the perplexing question, "What next? Should I begin work on a master's degree immediately, or should I teach for a while? Should I pursue master's work here, or should I go to another university? Which master's program should I pursue?" These are not easy questions to answer. There are probably as many answers to these questions as there are students and programs. Furthermore, the basic structure of the secondary school, which for years has been organized around the self-contained classroom, the subject-matter-oriented teacher, and the student who miraculously "changed interests" when the bell rang, is changing rapidly. The self-contained classroom is being replaced by large study centers, small discussion areas, large lecture halls, and laboratories. The subject-matter-oriented teacher is joining a team of teachers with expertise in the content area as well as in designing instructional strategies and media, diagnosing student problems, and prescribing instructional sequences for individual students. The bell is being replaced by modular scheduling, which may permit arranging the student's day to match his interest and capacity with the demands of the curriculum he is pursuing.

   The vast array of changes in the basic organization of the school will probably be surpassed in magnitude by the curricular changes. Two of these changes, individualized science instruction and unified high school science, are already integral components of many school science programs. Other curriculum reforms will attempt to satisfy student demands for relevance, recognition, and responsibility. Many secondary school students feel that the curriculum they pursue should be more relevant to them, that they should be recognized as students capable of intellectualizing, and that they should be given additional responsibility in determining the nature and course of their education.

Changes in the basic structure of the school and in the curriculum have led to a redefinition of the teacher's role and formation of the differentiated-teaching-faculty concept. The differentiated-teaching-faculty concept is evolving to meet the need for, and recognition of, teachers who can perform specialized functions within the school. Organizing a differentiated-teaching-faculty involves establishing job descriptions of the wide variety of functions teachers should perform, weighing the amount of time and intellectual activity demanded by each description, and assigning appropriate salaries. The following descriptions provide examples of some positions that may be available. Many other positions will, undoubtedly, be created to facilitate the transition of the computer from experimental gadget to co-manager of instruction.

1. Master teacher: Diagnostician-prescriber.
   a. Examines student's record, personality, and scores on criterion tests. Designs and writes prescriptions for students to follow. Outlines functions of other teachers. Evaluates prescriptions.
   b. Works until job is done.
   c. Has recognized expertise in science teaching, tests and measurement, evaluating available instructional materials, prescription writing, and the direction of other teachers.
2. Master teacher: actor.
   a. Is capable of a wide variety of teaching acts. An actor-teacher who can follow a prescription and assume many teaching roles. Works closely with the diagnostician-prescriber to develop and test prescriptions. Analyzes other teachers and assists them in developing teaching skill.
   b. Works until job is done.
   c. Has recognized expertise in acting out a prescribed role, relating to others, teaching, evaluating teaching performances.
3. Large-group teacher.
   a. Is an excellent speaker capable of communicating to a large group. Prepares large-group presentations suggested by prescription and evaluates the effectiveness of his presentation.

      b. May work an eight-hour day or may work with small groups in co-curricular activities.

      c. Has recognized expertise in science teaching and speaking.

  4. Small-group teacher.

      a. Works with small groups of students. Leads students into discussions of content, laboratory experiences, and other interactions between student and subject matter, or student and teacher and subject matter.

      b. Typically also has responsibilities to small groups other than regular classes: clubs, intramural sports, and so on.

      c. Has recognized expertise in science teaching, working with small groups of students, coordinating co-curricular activities.

  5. Instructional media specialist.

      a. Designs media for all teachers. Typically designs the media for prescriptions. Directs paraprofessionals in the preparation of materials, directs students to prepare media through audiovisual club or similar organization.

      b. May work an eight-hour day.

      c. Has recognized expertise in science teaching, preparing audiovisual materials, selecting and/or evaluating available audiovisual materials.

  6. Reading specialist.

      a. Works with individuals who have severe reading problems. Evaluates readability of all prepared materials. Suggests change to those who are preparing material.

      b. May work an eight-hour day. May also assume club or other co-curricular responsibilities.

      c. Has recognized expertise in teaching science, teaching reading, diagnosing reading problems of students, evaluating written materials.

  7. Programmer.

      a. Designs programs to fit prescriptions. Evaluates programs. Provides feedback to master teacher.

      b. May work an eight-hour day and never have direct contact with students or may conduct developmental testing of materials with a limited number of students.

      c. Has recognized expertise in designing and developing programs.

  8. Individual-help teacher.

      a. Works with individual students on enrichment or remedial activities. May provide instruction to the homebound.

    b. May work almost any number of hours.

    c. Has recognized expertise in science instruction of individual students.

9. Experience Organizer Teacher.

    a. Organizes material and equipment for other teachers which cannot be prepared by a paraprofessional.

    b. May work less than full time. (Could be a housewife and former teacher. Could perform some of her functions in her own home.)

    c. Has recognized expertise in science teaching.

10. Paraprofessional.

    a. Provides general assistance, typically nonacademic. Supervises some student activity. Prepares materials, supplies, and equipment for teachers.

    b. Works an eight-hour day.

    c. Has recognized expertise in technical knowledge of science.

Computer-assisted and computer-managed instruction is evolving as rapidly as the concept of the differentiated teaching faculty. In some schools differentiated faculties will initiate computer utilization. In other schools the purchase of computer time will precede faculty differentiation.

Computer-assisted instruction will probably precede computer-managed instruction in most schools. Initially, computers will be used to teach students knowledge level information and skills that teachers frequently teach by a drill method. Later computers will be programed to teach more sophisticated concepts and principles, carry on a dialogue with students, analyze student progress, and eventually write detailed prescriptions for individual students to follow. However, even when the computer seemingly takes over management responsibilities by writing prescriptions, the teacher will not be replaced. Teachers will be needed to diagnose student progress, feed information into computers, and prepare programs. Today a teacher may direct a student to a computer; tomorrow a computer may direct a student to a teacher. The teacher will not be replaced, but he will necessarily function in a different manner.

An obvious answer to the graduating senior's query concerning "What next?" is that he should think far beyond what he should do next year or which master's degree he should pursue. Rather than simply fulfilling requirements for a master's degree, he should be working toward becoming an excellent teacher, which would include

1. Gaining mastery of the science subject field.
2. Specializing in an area of education.

3. Working toward improving the teaching profession.

4. Designing and carrying out a plan for continued study.

Or he should be preparing for a nonteaching function within the school.

Toward Subject-Matter Mastery

Science teachers should be committed to pursuing mastery of the science subject area. Although command of the subject matter does not automatically make the individual a good teacher, it is an essential prerequisite of good teaching. Similarly, although knowing how to teach is an essential prerequisite to becoming a good teacher, an individual must also have an adequate command of the subject matter he is teaching.

Subject-matter mastery, when it is defined as knowing everything within a field, is essentially and practically impossible. Today a more pragmatic definition of subject-matter mastery is knowing enough about the area to continue studying the recent developments within the area. Even attaining this level of mastery demands considerable effort; furthermore, this effort must be persistent. The science teacher who does not continue his efforts as a student of science jeopardizes his present and future effectiveness as a science teacher.

The problem of attaining initial subject-matter competence within the field is, and will continue to be, complicated by the unification of the sciences. Yet in many states certification patterns permit teachers to complete most of their preparation within a single area, with only cursory attention given cognate areas. Teachers entering the profession without adequate training in cognate areas are literally "out of date" before they begin. They frequently need additional training or extensive study just to teach the major subject they thought they were being prepared to teach.

The essential questions are, "Are you prepared to teach science—not just earth science, biology, chemistry, or physics, but science?" "Do you have enough science background to see the relationships which exist between the sciences?" "Could you participate in planning and teaching a unified science course in the secondary school?" If your answers to all these questions are yes, you are atypical. Few college seniors are so prepared. If, however, you desire seriously to become and continue to be an effective science teacher, you should work toward preparing yourself to answer these questions affirmatively.

There is no single path leading directly to positive answers for all these questions. Some students will need additional formal training in courses and seminars. Others may continue their educational informally by reading recent books, articles, and even conducting research. The unavailability of adequate library facilities will prohibit many from studying science as actively as they should. The inaccessibility of a good library, while limiting, need not prohibit study of recent science developments. Journals, such as *Science* and *Scientific American*, can be purchased at very reasonable prices. Teachers should not only subscribe, they should study these magazines. A list of periodicals which should interest all science teachers may be found in the Appendix.

Specialization in Education

The self-contained class, taught by a single teacher, is becoming obsolete. Teachers who are trained and experienced in nothing other than managing and maintaining a self-contained classroom will discover that employment opportunities diminish, and they may even find themselves unemployable. Teachers with demonstrated subject-matter competence, as well as a specialization in one or more areas of professional education, will be in great demand. The great demand for educational specialists can be attributed to the technological innovations which have made individualized instruction a realistic goal for all students. The question, "Should I specialize in an area of professional education?" is as out of date as the single-teacher, single-classroom concept. The only appropriate question is, " *Which* area should I specialize in?"

The "model" team described earlier (see pp. 224) provides some indication of positions that may be available. In the following descriptions we will attempt to define specializations more precisely. You will notice that a considerable overlap of these skills may be desirable.

Diagnostician

The diagnostician will study the overt and covert activities of students involved in learning. He will examine physical activity as well as scores on criterion tests. He may, for example, observe the student's posture, motion, eye-pupil size, and other factors which may indicate the degree of student involvement in learning.

As a diagnostician, his main responsibility will be to determine if the student is proceeding successfully along the continuum designed by the prescriber. Although it is already possible to design computer-assisted instruction that is equal to or better than traditional classroom instruction for many students, it is presently impossible to do this for all students, and will probably continue to be impossible for several years. Computer-assisted instruction will thus create a need for diagnosticians; it will not replace teachers, but the teacher's role will be redefined.

Prescriber

The prescriber will either have to be a diagnostician or a consumer of information provided by diagnosticians. He will study the physical and mental characteristics of individual students and design a sequence of instruction which matches the individual's physical and mental capabilities. The prescriber will utilize computers extensively. Eventually computers will be programed to carry on many or most of the prescriber's activities.

Test Constructionist

The principal function of the test constructionist will be designing criterion tests. Initially, the need for test constructionists will be very high. However, once a large bank of test items is generated, matching test items to prescriptions will become a computer function. The test constructionist's major function eventually will involve revising existing questions, deleting questions, and writing new questions as new knowledge is inserted into the curriculum.

Actor-Teacher

The actor-teacher will be a proficient manipulator of a wide variety of teacher influences and combinations of teacher influences. He will be able to assume the roles of direct teacher, indirect teacher, or any combination of influences which have been hypothesized as a means of teaching a given concept to an individual or group of individuals who are not learning successfully. It is assumed that an ideal machine-operated curriculum, one which will permit *all* students to learn successfully, will never be developed. The actor-teacher will work with other members of a team to design new approaches to teaching a given concept or principle to students who are not learning successfully from the available machinery. Once this new approach is developed, it may well be programed into the computer and become another alternate path, or the computer may be programed to direct students who take this path to another type of experience. The *ideal machine-operated curriculum* will probably need an infinite number of paths. Hence the need to develop these alternate paths will probably continue indefinitely.

Programers

The discussion in Chapter 10 undoubtedly eliminates the need for an extensive description of what a programer will be doing in the secondary school. The only remaining question is, "How many programers will be needed?"

Instructional Communication Center

The school's Instructional Communication Center will evolve as much as or more than most areas within the school. It will become a huge library–planning–production center designed and staffed specifically to provide services to faculty and students. It will employ a wide variety of specialists and technicians. The specialists will include

1. Media designers and producers.
2. Programers.
3. Subject-matter specialists.
4. Audiovisual librarians.
5. Professional speakers.
6. Reading specialists.

The specific function of all these individuals will be to assist the other areas in the school in developing curricular materials. As the hypothesized gigantic educational parks become reality, each curricular area within the school may have its own specialized audiovisual department.

Discussion-Generators and Guides

The computer will probably never eliminate the need for student–student or student–teacher interaction. In fact, the teacher's role as a discussion generator and guide will become much more important. The teacher will no longer have to teach the facts. Computers can already teach facts more efficiently than most teachers. Eventually students may carry on dialogues with computers which may replace the need for some student–student or student–teacher interaction. However, in the immediate future there will be a great demand for teachers who can generate and guide student discussion. Furthermore, the population explosion will force schools to emphasize the development of interpersonal communication skills. It appears unlikely that computers will be able to replace the efficient discussion generator and leader for many years.

Teacher-Educators

Teacher education is not a four-, five-, or even a six-year endeavor; theoretically it is a continuous effort, and it must become one in actuality. The first function of a school system teacher–educator will be to help the novice make the transition from college student to functional member of the school's teaching team. Each school and each school population have unique features. The teacher–educator will help the novice (1) recognize, adapt to, and work with these features, (2) polish his teaching skills, and (3) guide the novice toward a specialization within the school that is congruent with his interest and his potential.

Second, the teacher–educator will continue to work with experienced teachers as they continue to polish their teaching skills and develop new skills.

The Total Picture

In the preceding paragraphs the teacher's role has been dissected. A dissected school, like a dissected animal, will probably not function properly. Someone will have to assemble it into an articulate, functional whole. This master-teacher, or master-organizer, will perform the most essential function within the school.

Improving the Teaching Profession

A single individual typically cannot, by himself, effect a great amount of change. Individuals need organizations and organizations need individuals if either is to function as an effective change agent.

There are several organizations of science teachers which need your support and, more particularly, your active participation. Although these organizations are relatively effective, each realizes that with more support and greater teacher participation they could be much more effective.

Science teacher organizations may be classified as general organizations that are designed to serve all science teachers and as specialized organizations designed specifically to emphasize the various disciplines of science. (See Appendix.) A science teacher should join and actively participate in at least one general organization and one specialized organization. For example, a biology teacher could join the National Science Teachers Association and the National Association of Biology Teachers.

The statement indicating that each teacher *should* join and participate in at least two professional science teachers organizations can be supported by examining the objectives of the various organizations. Each organization is attempting to

1. Improve science instruction.
2. Provide information to science teachers on the latest ideas and innovations in the teaching of science.
3. Serve as a forum where ideas can be advanced and discussed.
4. Lobby for improved conditions for science teachers which will permit the teacher to become more effective.

The teacher who actively participates in these organizations will contribute to the growth and development of the science teaching profession and realize that he is also gaining from the experience. Science teacher organizations need teachers, and teachers need the organizations!

Planning Continuous Study

The teacher must view himself as a student of science and a student of effective teaching practices. That is, the teacher *must* continue studying science and teaching as long as he remains in the classroom. Without continuous study the teacher is doomed to gain but one year of experience twenty times rather than gaining twenty full years of experience.

Designing a plan for continuous study can begin by assuming that as a beginning teacher you will undoubtedly profit from additional formal course work in both science and education. However, assuming that *any* course work which leads to a master's degree will be beneficial is probably erroneous. Universities are continually attempting to make the requirements for a master's degree more flexible to permit students to design a course of study that is most appropriate for them and their career objectives. Hence, it becomes vitally important that the student *think out* his objectives prior to designing his master's program. Students who simply piece together courses to have a good schedule, avoid a *tough* professor, or fulfill graduation requirements frequently discover that they are not any better prepared to become an effective teacher than they were when they received their bachelor's degree.

Designing career objectives can begin by asking, "What do I think I would like to do in the teaching profession?" "Is my dream realistic?" When these two questions have been answered, the individual should proceed by checking certification requirements and talking to professionals in the field (that is, individuals practicing in the secondary school as well as college professors). If certification requirements and discussions with professionals are encouraging, he should use the information he obtained from these sources to design a course of study. If he is discouraged by the information he receives, he should re-examine his objectives. Abandoning the objectives may be a mistake, but continuing on without considering alternatives may be a bigger mistake.

Formal course work beyond the master's degree is typically feasible and advisable. However, the same caution should be used; avoid simply taking another course. Select courses that will contribute to your progress as a student of science and education. Eventually you may have to pursue most of your study informally by reading the journals and recent books and conducting research in science and education.

Nonteaching Functions

Schools will continue to need administrators and guidance counselors. Science teachers with the interest and the potential to become effective administrators or guidance counselors should consider pursuing careers in these areas. Teachers interested in these areas should follow the same steps outlined earlier: (1) talk with professionals in the field, (2) study certification requirements, and (3) think. Promotion of the ineffective teacher or coach with a losing season to a position in administration or guidance is rare. Administration and guidance, like teaching, need people with interest and potential. Becoming an excellent administrator or guidance counselor requires specific characteristics. Remember, an outstanding teacher might become a poor administrator, and an outstanding administrator could be a poor teacher.

Discussion Questions

1. You have just finished serving on the committee which selected the nation's ten best teachers for the year 1990. Describe these teachers. Include descriptions of their attitudes, cognitive abilities, and skills.
2. Assume that you would like to be named to the list of top ten teachers of the year 1990. How will you prepare yourself?

Additional References

Brown, Billye W., and Walter R. Brown. *Science Teaching and the Law*. Washington, D.C.: National Science Teachers Association, 1969.

Hammonds, Carsie. *Teaching Vocations*. Interstate Printers & Publishers, 1968.

Hurd, Paul DeHart. *New Curriculum Perspectives for Junior High School Science*. Belmont, Calif.: Wadsworth Publishing Company, 1970.

Kelly, Win. *Teaching in the Community Junior College*. New York: Appleton-Century-Crofts, 1970.

McLuhan, Marshall, and Quentin Fiore. *The Medium Is the Massage*. New York: Bantam Books, Inc., 1967.

NSTA. *A Career for You as a Science Teacher*. Washington, D.C.: National Science Teachers Association, 1966.

NSTA. *Keys to Careers in Science and Technology*. Washington, D.C.: National Science Teachers Association, 1970.

Skinner, B. F. *The Technology of Teaching*. Des Moines, Ia.: Meredith, 1968.

Trow, William Clark. *Teacher and Technology: New Designs for Learning*. Des Moines, Ia.: Meredith, 1963.

Trump, J. Lloyd, and Delmas F. Miller. *Secondary School Curriculum Improvement: Proposals and Procedures*. Boston: Allyn & Bacon, 1968.

appendix:
science periodicals particularly
valuable for the
high school science teacher

Science Education : General

The Science Teacher
National Science Teachers Association

1201 Sixteenth Street, N.W.
Washington, D.C. 20036

Journal of Research in Science Teaching
National Association for Research in
Science Teaching
Dr. T. Wayne Taylor
Science and Mathematics Teaching
Center Michigan State University
East Lansing, Michigan 48823

School Science and Mathematics
Central Association of Science
& Mathematics Teachers
P.O. Box 246
Bloomington, Indiana 47401

Science Education : Areas

Journal of Geological Education
National Association of Geology
  Teachers
c/o Roy Ingram, Treasurer
Department of Geology
University of North Carolina
Chapel Hill, North Carolina 27515

Geotimes
National Association of Geology
  Teachers
c/o Roy Ingram, Treasurer
University of North Carolina
Chapel Hill, North Carolina 27515

The American Biology Teacher
National Association of Biology
  Teachers
1420 N. Street, N.W.
Washington, D.C. 20005

Chemistry
American Chemical Society
1155 16th Street, N.W.
Washington, D.C. 20036

The Journal of Chemical Education
American Chemical Society
Division of Chemical Education
20th and Northampton Street
Easton, Pennsylvania 18042

The Physics Teacher
American Association of Physics
  Teachers
335 East 45th Street
New York, New York 10017

Science Periodicals

Science
American Association for the Advancement of Science
1515 Massachusetts Avenue, N.W.
Washington, D.C. 20005

Scientific American
415 Madison Avenue
New York, 10017

Science Digest
Science Digest, Inc.
200 E. Ontario
Chicago, Illinois 60611

Bio Science
American Institute of Biological Sciences
3900 Wisconsin Avenue, N.W.
Washington, D.C. 20016

Sky & Telescope
Sky Publishing Corporation
Harvard University Observatory
Cambridge, Massachusetts 02138

Chemical Engineering News
American Chemical Society
1155 16th Street, N.W.
Washington, D.C. 20036

Physics Today
American Institute of Physics
335 East 45th Street
New York, New York, 10017

Science Newsletter
Science Service, Inc.
1719 N. Street, N.W.
Washington, D.C. 20005

index